58971

Contents

A Caregiver's Bill of Rights

I have the right:

1. to take care of myself. This is not an act of self-ishness. It will give me the capability of taking better care of my loved one.

2. to seek help from others even though my loved one may object. I recognize the limits of my own endurance and strength.

3. to maintain facets of my own life that do not include the person I care for, just as I would if he or she were healthy. I know that I do everything that I reasonably can for this person, and I have the right to do some things just for myself.

4. to get angry, be depressed, and express other difficult feelings occasionally.

5. to reject any attempt by my loved one (either conscious or unconscious) to manipulate me through guilt, anger, or depression.

6. to receive consideration, affection, forgiveness, and acceptance for what I do from my loved one for as long as I offer these qualities in return.

7. to take pride in what I am accomplishing and to applaud the courage it has sometimes taken to meet the needs of my loved one.

8. to protect my individuality and my right to make a life for myself that will sustain me in the time when my loved one no longer needs my full-time help.

9. to expect and demand that as new strides are made in finding resources to aid physically and mentally impaired older persons in our country, similar strides will be made toward aiding and supporting caregivers.

Add your own rights to this list on the back of this page. Read this list to yourself every day.

_____

_____

_____

_____

_____

_____

_____

_____

_____

_____

_____

_____

_____

_____

Caring for the Caregiver

Under-
standing

CHAPTER 1

Understanding Alzheimer's

*Lucky is he
who has been able
to understand the
causes of things.*

Virgil
(Roman poet)

Someone you love has been diagnosed with Alzheimer's disease. You suddenly find yourself with a job you never wanted, never planned for, and never trained for. You are the nurse, the cook, the servant, the parent, the punching bag. You are the **Caregiver.** This book is for you.

It's designed to take you through the basics of patient care and to give you the information you'll need to help guide you through the medical, legal, and financial issues that accompany Alzheimer's disease.

There are chapters on taking care of yourself, medical research and treatments, financial and legal issues, home safety, day-to-day concerns, and support groups. The final chapter is called "The Patient Profile," and it consists of categories you can fill in to create a profile of the patient. This profile will help you keep an organized schedule of the patient's activities and needs, and it will be an invaluable tool for any caregiver who takes your place temporarily or permanently. In addition, throughout the book there are addresses, book lists, product lists, and hot line numbers. The hot line numbers can help connect you to people you can talk to and count on.

Chapter 8 (The Patient Profile) is for your input. Use it to write in the most important and current information about the **Patient.** This information will make it possible for another caregiver to take your place and give you a rest from a responsibility that sometimes may overwhelm you.

The Patient Profile

As much as possible, try to maintain your sense of humor—it is important to helping you maintain an emotionally healthy life. Laughter is a potent defense against the darker side of caregiving; so when you're uptight or exhausted, finding something to laugh about can be the key to easing your burden.

This guidebook is no substitute for your physician or professional advisers. It's a reinforcement of the things your physician will tell you. More importantly, it's your guide through the difficult days ahead—and your daily reminder that there are many who care about you, the caregiver.

The Symptoms of Alzheimer's Disease

Alzheimer's disease is a type of dementia. Dementia is the term used to describe a serious decline of intellectual functions, including memory and the ability to think.[1]

All people with Alzheimer's disease have symptoms of loss of memory and intellectual ability, but the symptoms are not identical for everyone. The rate at which the symptoms grow worse or increase in number varies as well. But whatever the pattern of symptoms, most of the following symptoms can occur:

The Most Common Symptoms:[2]

- Loss of memory, decreased ability to learn, and decreased attention span
- Loss of thinking ability, judgment, and decision making
- Loss of ability to recall the appropriate word or phrase
- Loss of mathematical ability
- Disorientation: gets lost; can't find way home
- Loss of physical coordination: inability to perform skilled motor acts
- Changes in personality: the outgoing person may become withdrawn; the loving person may become uncaring
- Changes in emotion, including agitation, depression, and suspiciousness
- Loss of initiative; indifferent

The Hardest Symptoms for Victims to Deal With:

- Loss of ability to communicate
- Loss of ability to recall family members and/or close friends

- Difficulty with common tasks, like driving a car[3]
- Loss of independence
- Awareness of memory changes

In Addition to Those Listed Above, the Hardest Symptoms for Caregivers to Deal With:

- Confusion and inability to follow instructions
- Inability to perform daily tasks
- Repetition of phrases and stories
- Wandering
- Loss of social inhibition (public displays of sexuality)
- Accusations of sexual misbehavior and of stealing
- Changes in personality, including rage and withdrawal
- Verbal profanity when outside of normal personality
- Refusal to give up driving car[4]

The Stages of Alzheimer's Disease

In reading the following paragraphs about the stages of Alzheimer's disease, don't try to picture yourself and the one you love at each stage. The things you fear most may never happen—your imaginings may be far worse than the realities. Be prepared, but take life one day at a time. There will be good days and bad days.

Early Stage

Symptoms.[2] In the early stage, your loved one may tend to have symptoms of forgetfulness, absentmindedness, and fatigue. There is some inability to recall common words and learn new things. Judgment and intellectual and social functioning seem faulty.

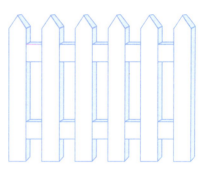

Concerns. Although most patients at this stage can carry out daily tasks without much difficulty, you may need to help with decisions about finances, relationships, and substantial life changes. Start thinking about the many day-to-day tasks the patient will eventually need help with, such as bathing, grooming, toileting, dressing, eating, exercising, and communicating.

And, at this stage, it's also important to think about how caring for the patient is going to affect you. In addition to following many of the suggestions in the chapters that follow, make a commitment to maintain your sense of humor—at least as much as possible.

In caring for the patient, enjoy the funny moments. For example, there is the story of an early-stage patient who thought her widower neighbor of 20 years had fallen in love with her. When family members asked her why, she said, "He brought me this squash from his garden this morning. He's never given me squash, only string beans." The patient will say amusing things like this, and it's okay to laugh at them because they *are* humorous.

Possible actions. Now you need to decide on a physician for continuing care. Talk with your loved one and other relatives about the immediate and long-term future: consider issues like living wills and durable power of attorney and adult day care services or long-term care services, such as skilled nursing facilities, health-related facilities, or combined facilities. Start thinking about what plans will need to be made.

NOTE: **Whether to tell someone they have Alzheimer's disease remains controversial. You should discuss this with your physician.**

Recognizing that someone has an incurable disease begins the grieving process for you. You will grieve for the loss of "self" that happens *now* and throughout the course of the disease. This is an *important* and necessary step toward coming to terms with Alzheimer's. Remember that feelings of grief are normal and will help you make a healthy emotional adjustment to the eventual loss of the patient.

Middle Stage

Symptoms.[5] When the disease reaches the middle stage, the following symptoms may appear more frequently:

- Loss of logic and decreased memory and motor ability

- Inability to be patient
- Wandering or pacing—the patient may follow you around the house, for example
- Striking out verbally or physically
- Slower speech and verbal understanding
- Diminishing mathematical skills
- Deteriorating social skills
- Paranoia
- Suspicion that people are watching and stealing
- Hiding things
- More aggressive behavior in response to frustration
- Resists offers of help

Concerns. The patient's unpredictability and loss of basic skills can make daily life trying for the patient and you. His or her increasing inability to perform skilled tasks—such as driving, cooking, sewing, or using tools—may lead to unsafe situations as well as anger-producing frustrations. Loss of motor skills also increases the person's chances of tripping or falling. Keep in mind, too, that occasionally symptoms temporarily disappear. Enjoy these moments, but try to resist thinking that the patient is "getting better" permanently.

Possible actions. The patient needs increasing supervision and help with daily activities. Now issues of safety inside and outside the house are of prime importance. Give instructions clearly, slowly, and in writing. Control social situations closely. Obtain financial and legal advice—patients at this stage are no longer able to manage their own finances.

> Do not overestimate the patient's abilities or think that he or she is being purposely difficult. Remember, patients cannot control their behavior.

Intimacy[6]/Sexuality

If you're married to the patient and you want to have sex with the patient, that's okay. There's no reason not to be intimate with the person. On the other hand, the patient may wish to have sexual relations with you even though you no longer want intimacy with the patient. You may feel it's unreasonable, for example. That's okay, too. You have a right to feel that way. When that happens, couples often find it helpful to sleep in separate beds, or even separate rooms.

The sex drive of the Alzheimer's patient will diminish and finally disappear. It's helpful to be open with yourself, and with family and friends, about the pain and loneliness you feel as a result of the changes in the patient's sexual behavior and the loss of intimacy you experience.

Patients at this stage of the disease may grab at strangers, touch themselves inappropriately, expose themselves, or demonstrate paranoia related to intimacy. This is particularly common for married patients, where accusations of sexual misbehavior, for example, may be set off by as little as seeing the spouse with another person. This paranoia is part of the disease and cannot be reasoned or argued away. It may be helpful to increase the amount of physical contact you have with the patient: hugging, brushing hair, patting, stroking.

Advanced Stage

Symptoms.[2] As the disease becomes more severe, patients may lose the ability to control their bladder or bowels, becoming incontinent. The ability to speak or follow simple commands diminishes. Hallucinations often appear now, and patients may respond physically—waving away snakes or hiding from monsters. Emotionally, they may become abusive, removed, or unresponsive.

As the intellectual loss increases, many Alzheimer's disease patients become calmer and less distressed at the changes in themselves because they cannot truly remember the way things used to be. Symptoms may seem to disappear for short periods, and the patient may seem to return to a more usual emotional state.

Concerns. At this stage, you will become deeply concerned about the patient's inability to respond to surroundings. Physical well-being is also a concern—and so is your own emotional well-being. Your loved one,

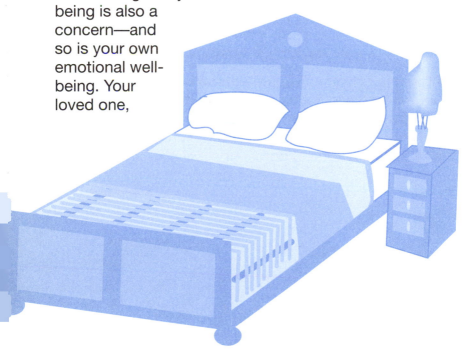

who may not always recognize you, is not as emotionally at risk as you are.

Possible actions. Now is the time to review the plans you have for continuing care and to ensure that all legal and financial affairs are in order.

The Final Stage

Symptoms.[7] At this stage patients lose almost all intellectual abilities, almost all speech and motor coordination, and all memory. They recognize no one and remember nothing. The "self" is gone.

Concerns. Comfort care is all that is possible at this stage. The patient needs to be bedded, bathed, and protected from harm. This stage is heart breaking for you, but keep in mind that the patient's suffering is over, as he or she is no longer capable of understanding what is going on. When the patient reaches the final stage, he or she may be in a long-term care facility of some kind, so it may be helpful to think about how you would deal with this situation.

Possible actions. Prepare yourself to resume your normal life-style, to resume the friendships and social outlets you've enjoyed in the past. For example, if the patient is now receiving long-term care by someone else or is in a nursing home, you will now have more time to devote to your normal activities like

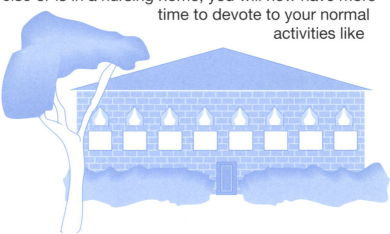

exercising, seeing friends, enjoying hobbies. Recognize that you have done all that you could have done. Think about all the positive, helpful assistance you have given the patient over the last years, and realize that he or she would be overjoyed with your help if he or she had the ability to recognize it. It may be helpful to make a list of things you've done for the patient. It's good to give yourself a pat on the back at this point. And if you think of things you could have done but didn't do, forgive yourself for it. No caregiver can do everything for a patient.

Courage is a kind of salvation.

Plato
(Greek philosopher)

Further Reading

AD Newsletter. Published quarterly through Alzheimer's Disease and Related Disorders Association, 70 East Lake Street, Chicago, Illinois 60601.

Aronson MK, ed. *Understanding Alzheimer's Disease.* New York: Charles Scribner's Sons, 1988. A publication of the Alzheimer's Disease and Related Disorders Association.

Carroll DL. *When Your Loved One Has Alzheimer's.* New York: Harper & Row/Perennial Library, 1990.

Frank J. *The Silent Epidemic.* Minneapolis: Learner Publications Company, 1985. (An introduction to Alzheimer's disease written especially for teenagers but helpful to many others.)

Mace NL, Rabins PV. *The 36-Hour Day.* Baltimore: The Johns Hopkins University Press—1991 Revised. Available from Warner Books, New York.

Q and A on Alzheimer's. Available free from the National Institute on Aging. Write ADEAR Center, P.O. Box 8250, Silver Spring, Maryland 20907. Ask for Publication Z-06.

Caring

CHAPTER 2

Caring for a Caregiver

*If anything is sacred;
the human body
is sacred.*

Walt Whitman
(American poet)

You're important, too! No one has to tell you that taking care of someone with Alzheimer's disease, 24 hours a day, day in and day out, is an exhausting and emotionally draining job. Yet many caregivers put aside their own needs and wants and spend all their energy on the patient.

One day these people may collapse under the strain. Don't be one of them. Take care of yourself.

Don't Become a Martyr: Jan's Story

When Jan was told that her 58-year-old mother, with whom she lived, had Alzheimer's disease, she affirmed her devotion by committing all her time and energy to her mother's care. Despite all she had read and had been told by her mother's physician, Jan was convinced that by sheer force of will she could arrest the progression of the disease. Refusing the assistance of relatives and friends, Jan found it necessary to take a leave of absence from her job so that she could care for her mother.

Leaving the house only to shop for food and other necessities, Jan became more and more reclusive. Friends' telephone calls were not returned. With no income, family savings, accumulated over many years, began to dwindle. Despite Jan's efforts, her mother progressed through the stages of Alzheimer's disease as would normally be expected. Even with all the best plans, Jan didn't realize things would happen fast. She realized too late that the disease followed a predictably downhill course in spite of her best intentions. When she could no longer physically care for her mother and placement in a long-term care facility was inevitable, Jan became profoundly depressed.

RESULT: **Regardless of the overt and unconscious motives behind Jan's devotion, the end result was the same. However, while there had been only one person in need of help, now there are two.**

Don't Become Embittered: Charles's Story

After 40 years of marriage, Charles and Pauline were just beginning to enjoy his retirement. Although they had recently moved to Arizona and were still adjusting to the community, Charles could not ignore the personality changes in Pauline. The diagnosis of Alzheimer's disease was a shock, but Charles's realization that his wife would become more and more dependent on him was worse. He felt overwhelmed and incapable of caring for her. Being in a new home and knowing few people, he also felt isolated. Having looked forward to his retirement for years, he cursed this cruel turn of events and resented the loss of his wife and the plans they had made together.

Although Pauline remained functional at home, Charles elected to place her in a nursing facility relatively early in the course of her disease. He was tormented by a responsibility he felt he could not assume and wanted the freedom of retirement. After Pauline's death, Charles became inconsolable.

RESULT: Anger and guilt are normal emotions for caregivers. You as the caregiver *do* have an obligation to yourself. But you are also important to the patient. That's why the most responsible and loving thing you can do for your patient is to *stay mentally and physically strong and keep yourself healthy.* Here are some suggestions on how to do that.

Keeping Well

Stay Physically Fit

Get enough rest. Alzheimer's patients often wander or pace at night, disturbing others' sleep. Find someone to be "on duty" at night while you sleep. If you can't afford the extra help, perhaps a relative or neighbor can replace you for a couple of hours in the afternoon while you nap. Or find relief through your support group or state assistance program. No matter where help comes from, it's important that you get it.

Eat a balanced diet. Seem obvious? There are too many caregivers who overlook this principle. When one is tired and tense from constant caregiving, it's easy to fall into the toast-and-tea habit. Guard against it. Do your best to include the basic food groups in your diet every day.

American Heart Association Suggestions[8]

- Limit salt intake and highly salted foods—take the salt shaker off the table and you're halfway there.

- Eat foods low in saturated fats and cholesterol—avoid red meat, fried foods, rich desserts.

- Include fiber in your diet—that means lots of fresh fruit, vegetables, and cereal.

- Maintain your weight. Many Alzheimer's patients gain or lose weight, but you don't have to. Don't diet—just don't overeat or undereat, and you'll be fine.

- Go easy on caffeine and sweets—too much coffee or sugar could put you on edge and make caregiving more difficult.

Exercise

Exercise can help reduce stress, but it also can drain precious excess energy from the patient. Check with your doctor and then follow his or her recommendations for a sensible exercise plan.

Many caregivers have found diverse and creative ways of fitting exercise into their schedule. Some take their patient with them as they walk laps around a local mall. (Patients may walk along. Or if they use a wheelchair, caregivers may wheel them around.) Many patients will sit contentedly and wait while their caregiver swims at a local pool, does aerobics, or walks around a track. Perhaps you could have a neighbor stay with the patient for a short time while you take an exercise break.

Stay Emotionally Healthy

So much depends on your emotional well-being. You must give yourself some personal time—time for *you* and the things you enjoy doing without having to constantly wait on or worry about the patient with Alzheimer's. In short, you should not feel guilty for taking time out to do things you enjoy, because staying emotionally healthy is important for your own health, and because it will, in the long run, make you a better caregiver.

Try to keep laughter in your life, too. Remember, maintaining your sense of humor, an issue discussed earlier, is important to helping you maintain your emotional health. Laughter is one of your most powerful weapons against the darker side of caregiving. When tensions run high and energy runs low, looking at the lighter side (or the ridiculous side!) can lighten your emotional load.

Here are some hints for carving out that personal time and enjoying yourself when you finally get it.

Change the scene. Get out of the house as much as you can. Walking is a great way to reduce stress, even if it's only for a few minutes. Get some fresh air and sunlight. Or watch the stars come out.

Call a friend. Sometimes you can't get out. If that happens, call a friend or family member who can cheer you up and offer support. The phone is right there. Use it as a support line.

Ask for help. Let others take a turn once in a while so that you can shop, have a meal, or go to a movie. Family members or friends can take turns so you can take a break.

Take time out. If you plan ahead carefully and make sure someone is "on duty," you can take a break—several hours off, or a whole day, if possible. The important thing is to "recharge your batteries." Above all, try not to lose touch with your friends and overall social network. Don't cut yourself off from socializing because it will hurt you emotionally in the long run, both personally and as a caregiver. *Make time* for yourself. But be honest with your friends. Tell them that your life is changing and that, if they haven't heard from you in a while, they should call you or get in touch with you somehow. Assure them that you value their friendship, that you care about them.

Be social. If you find yourself feeling isolated, renew old ties with friends you haven't communicated with in a while, or build new ties with new friends. It's important to maintain existing friendships—and to make new ones.

Hang on to your hobbies. Reading, cooking, music, whatever—your hobbies and interests help keep you "plugged in" to life. Keep doing the things you enjoy; don't give up activities that refresh your mind and heart.

Treat yourself. Do something nice for *you.* Buy a new jacket; take yourself to dinner or to a concert. Enjoy!

Before Stress Happens

Taking care of yourself is the first step in managing stress, but when you feel stress, keep in mind that your stress, the stress you show, can be misinterpreted by patients—making them stressed and anxious. The following method is a great way to guard against imminent stress. Here's how it works:

- Continue breathing normally. Do not hold your breath when confronted with a stressful situation.

- Keep your facial expression normal, too. If you can manage it, even a tiny smile will go a long way toward preventing an over-reaction by the nervous system.

- Maintain your posture. Don't "cave in" to stress by sagging over into a slouch.

- Create a mental picture of your tension being released.

- Focus on how to keep control of the situation. Try to accept what is happening so that it can be understood and dealt with properly.

- Practice these approaches and use them at the very beginning of each situation. Soon you will find yourself more often solving problems than screaming because of them.

Reduce Stress

When the stress and strain of daily caregiving start to sap your energy, take a break. Go for a walk; sit alone; listen to music—find a way to relax. If you don't have a relaxing hobby, think of one and try it. How about gardening, renting and watching movies, playing bingo or chess, doing needlepoint or wood-working, or doing photography or painting? If none of these appeal to you, ask friends for suggestions. Some people tap into the stress-reducing potential of relaxation techniques such as meditation and yoga. The YMCA offers low-cost courses in the basics of these techniques, as do many local health clubs and churches. If you're stressed out, try this:

- Lie or sit in a comfortable quiet place.
- Close your eyes and make tight fists.
- Hold for five seconds. Relax. Then note how the tension seems to drain away.
- Repeat three times, each time noting the tension/relaxation contrast.
- Now repeat the same process through-out the various muscle groups of the body (arms, shoulders, legs, back, thighs, feet, etc)
- Focus all your attention on the feeling of release as you relax the muscles in a given group.

Slow Down With Classical Music

Listening to classical music can also have a calming effect on people. Here are a few sugges-tions for classical music pieces with a slow rhythm:

- Bach's Brandenburg Concerto No. 4, 2nd movement
- Bach's Orchestral Suite No. 2 ("Saraband")
- Holst's The Planets ("Venus")
- Ravel's Mother Goose Suite, 1st Movement

The "Sun Salutation"

The sun salutation is the name of a group of yoga postures that are useful in stretching and relaxing the body. It is an easy technique that can be used anytime, anywhere. The process goes like this:

- Begin by standing with your feet together, toes straight ahead.
- Bring left foot forward and right foot backward. (Keep toes pointed straight.)
- Raise left arm straight overhead, while keeping right arm at your side.
- Now bend knees slightly and tip entire torso back slightly.
- Breathe regularly and hold for about 10 seconds.
- Reverse to other side and repeat. (You will feel this stretch under the beltline on each side.)

(Interested in learning more? There is a 75-minute home video entitled "Yoga for Beginners," with a companion 52-page book of instructions. For a copy, call Healing Arts Home Video at 1-800-722-7347.)

The "Heavenly Stretch"

This exercise can also help ease tension during the day.

- In a quiet place, stand straight with feet together and eyes forward. Exhale.
- Then inhale slowly and stretch your arms as high as you can.
- Lift up your toes and reach skyward as you imagine a thread running up through your spine pulling you up.
- Reach and reach some more! As you reach, continue to inhale bits of air as long as you possibly can.
- Then exhale slowly, slowly. As you let your arms

descend slowly, flex your wrists and push palms downward.

Massage Therapy

Lately, people have begun rediscovering how benefi-cial massage therapy can be for stress control. You could also consider massage treatments for the patient you care for—treatments by you or an experi-enced masseuse. You and the patient could even perform massage therapy on each other.

Massage helps. If you would like more information about massage therapy, call the American Massage Therapy Association at 312-761-AMTA for recom-mendations in your area.

Get support for yourself. Acknowledge that it's okay to seek support. You may need help or advice to learn how to do something for the patient, or you may need support to han-dle the physical, emotional, or psychological drain that can affect you as a result of caring for the patient. Seeking support is not a sign of weakness. It's the sensible thing to do. Caregivers report that support groups make a real difference in reminding them they are not alone.

Keep Your Spirits Up

One way to keep your attitude and outlook positive is by being open to laughter. A lot of amusing events often take place around a patient with Alzheimer's. Consider, for example, the story of an early-stage patient who for many years had taken great pride in preparing dinner for her extended family every

Sunday. Despite suggestions that she relinquish the responsibility, the patient insisted that the dinners continue. While baking a cake one Sunday morning she added white pepper instead of sugar to the mix. This resulted not from her misidentifying the pepper but rather from her inability to remember which should be added to a cake mix. Her error was discovered only after family members had taken the first bites into what looked like her usually delicious pastry. Everyone quickly reached for their drinks, and they all had a chuckle afterwards.

In addition to humor, some people find religion to be a comfort, a way of keeping positive, in times of trouble. If this is true for you, you might look for a house of worship in which you feel welcome and comfortable—somewhere you can find strength and a sense of renewal.

Sometimes caregivers with religious faith feel angry that God could let this terrible affliction happen to the patient—and to them. Then they feel guilty for feeling angry, even though it's okay to be angry—it's natural. Talking with your priest, rabbi, or minister can help remind you that anger is a very human response and give you the reassurance that you're not alone. Don't punish yourself with guilt, and don't try to be a martyr.

If you are really overwhelmed, seek special help; guilt, anger, despair, and hopelessness are all common feelings for caregivers. But the question is to what degree are you feeling these emotions? Are you up all night worrying? Are you losing weight? Are you drinking in excess? Are you using too many prescription medications? Are you considering suicide? These are all strong indicators.

Ultimately, though, it's a matter of listening to your own feelings. If you truly feel that you just cannot cope any longer, then you can't, and you need help. Although it may sound oversimplified, it really does hold true. If you *think* you need help, you do. There are a number of ways to find a support group or a counselor. You can ask family and friends, your clergyman, or your doctor. You can also check with community health clinics or religious-affiliated service agencies like the Jewish Family and Children's Society, Associated Catholic Charities, or pastoral counseling services. Your local county medical society can provide names of local psychiatrists as well. If you do join a support group, remember that it's okay just to sit and listen. You *don't have* to talk.

Not all counselors are knowledgeable about caregiving for the patient with Alzheimer's and its related problems. Select a counselor carefully, and if, after a fair amount of time, you feel your needs are not being met, consider finding a different individual. The Alzheimer's Disease Education and Referral Center (800-438-4380) and the Alzheimer's Disease and Related Disorders Association (312-335-8700) can help answer your questions about identifying a suitable counselor.

Prayer as a Resource

For those whose spiritual beliefs are founded in religion, the power of prayer can offer a profound sense of comfort. Prayer has the potential to fill the void created when hopelessness seems to loom above all else. This is because prayer, to those who use it, is based on the premise that God will never leave them, that He will always be there to lift and to heal. And in knowing this, in knowing that they are never really battling alone, those who pray have a powerful resource to which they can turn in times of need.

> **Many people have found comfort in the Serenity Prayer: "Grant me the serenity to accept the things I cannot change, the courage to change the things I can, and the wisdom to know the difference."**

Grief

Mourning for a person with Alzheimer's disease is a long process. It has no set timetable, as there is after a death. It seems to go on and on. Piece by piece, you mourn the loss of a human intellect, a personality—of everything that makes a person a person. And yet, you do not even have the comfort of the public ceremonies of mourning, because the person's body is still alive. Many people find that sharing these feelings with others in similar situations, such as support groups, brings renewed strength. Regardless, keep in mind that grieving for the patient is absolutely normal in this situation. Indeed, it's a *necessary* step in the experience of caring for an Alzheimer's patient.

*The quality of mercy
is not strained;
it droppeth as the
gentle rain from heaven.*

Shakespeare
(English playwright)

Further Reading

Cooper R, PhD. *Health and Fitness Excellence.* New York: Houghton Mifflin Company, 1989.

Epstein G, MD. *Healing Visualizations: Creating Health Through Imagery.* New York: Bantam, 1989.

Ornish D, MD. *Dean Ornish's Program for Reversing Heart Disease.* New York: Random House, 1990.

Medical

CHAPTER 3

Medical Update

There is nothing without a reason.
Gottfried Wilhelm Leibniz
(German philosopher)

Dr. Alois Alzheimer, a German physician, first described the kind of dementia your loved one is suffering from in a research paper in 1907.[5] For many years, the symptoms we now associate with Alzheimer's disease were thought to be the result of "hardening of the arteries" or "the decline of aging."

Today medical researchers know that the mental (and eventually physical) deterioration associated with this disease is the result of actual loss of brain cells.

Alzheimer's by the numbers (data from the Progress Report on Alzheimer's Disease, 1992; from the Alzheimer's Disease Education and Referral Center, Silver Spring, MD; 1993):

- There are now about 4 million Alzheimer's victims nationwide.
- By the year 2040, Alzheimer's disease may afflict more than 12 million Americans.
- Alzheimer's disease is the fourth leading cause of death in the United States.
- As of the most recent accounting, the yearly

cost of Alzheimer's and other dementia care is
$90 billion.

Some Suspected Causes

Though research on Alzheimer's disease has
increased at a rapid pace in the last decade, the
cause of the disease has not been established. There
are a number of possible causes under investigation.

Cholinergic hypothesis.[9] The cholinergic hypothesis is based on the activity of acetylcholine (ACh), a
chemical substance found in the brain. This substance carries the signals from nerve cell to nerve
cell and is involved in correctly processing the
brain's commands regarding thought and behavior
functions. Explained in its simplest terms, this
hypothesis says that decreases in ACh activity
occur in the brains of patients with Alzheimer's disease. This decrease in ACh activity, the theory
argues, is a key reason for the memory loss and
other brain-related problems associated with
Alzheimer's disease.

Beta-amyloid protein.[10] Another area of research
regarding the cause of Alzheimer's disease concerns
a protein called beta-amyloid. It is found in the brains
of Alzheimer's victims. Some researchers believe this
protein plays a basic role in the development of
Alzheimer's, possibly triggering the degeneration of
brain cells. Others argue that beta-amyloid is merely
a "marker" of disease—the result, but not the cause,
of Alzheimer's.

Genetic factors.[11] A great deal of research has been
conducted on the genetic issues surrounding
Alzheimer's. For most family members this research
has shown only a slight increase in their chances of
developing the disease. One hereditary pattern that
scientists have noticed, however, is a greater inci-
dence of Alzheimer's in the family members of those

victims who acquire the disease early (ie, before age 50). Researchers have concluded there is a definite genetic link in those families. Such genetic patterns are determined biologically.

Environmental toxins.[12] Another area of research concerns environmental poisons or toxins. No one knows if this is the cause of the disease or the result. All studies done so far have not supported this theory.

A slow-acting virus.[13] Research in this area is based on the suspicion that a virus attacks brain cells. The virus attack, it's believed, changes brain chemistry and causes cell deterioration. So far investigations have not supported this theory. And there is no evidence that Alzheimer's disease can be passed from one person to another.

What about brain autopsy? The only definite diagnosis of Alzheimer's disease is made by finding physical changes in the brain.[14] Your physician may ask that you permit a brain autopsy of your loved one to definitely confirm the diagnosis of Alzheimer's disease or to help in research. For information or advice, contact any of the support organizations listed in Chapter 7 and talk to your family, friends, clergyman, or lawyer. Ultimately, the decision to donate brain tissue from the patient is yours.

Other Causes of Dementia[7]

There are treatable causes of dementia, such as Vitamin B_{12} deficiency or prescription drug interactions, to name a few. In diagnosing Alzheimer's disease, however, your doctor has ruled out these causes.

Be Aware of Drug Side Effects

Some drugs can cause or increase confusion in elderly patients. Some of these may be:[15]

- Antidepressant medications
- Nervous system-related medications
- Blood pressure medications
- Heart medications
- Narcotic pain killers
- Antiarthritic medications
- Anti-Parkinson's medications
- Tranquilizers
- Barbiturates (for sleep)
- Medications to stop involuntary muscle actions

Whenever you visit the patient's physician, bring a list of the patient's medications, both prescription and nonprescription types.

Treatment Available Now

When a person is struck by Alzheimer's disease, key brain cells involved in important memory circuits degenerate. Along with this, a significant reduction of acetylcholine in the brain occurs.[16] This deficiency of acetylcholine is believed to cause some of the symptoms of Alzheimer's disease.

The resultant progressive, degenerative disease disrupts the flow of information in the brain, leading to problems with memory, thinking, and behavior. These problems get worse in time as the physical changes in the brain become more severe.

The latest advance in the treatment of dementia of the Alzheimer's type is a new drug called Cognex® (tacrine hydrochloride capsules)10, 20, 30,

40 mg, from Parke-Davis. In clinical studies, Cognex® has provided some benefits for Alzheimer's disease patients in the early stages of the disease. Specifically, Cognex has helped some patients in clinical studies who have taken the drug for between 12 and 30 weeks to evaluate the drug's effectiveness. Patients who took Cognex showed treatment effects on measures of cognitive performance.[17] These results were seen by physicians.

Although it is not certain how Cognex works, it presumably acts by increasing the level of acetyl-choline activity in the brain of patients in the early stages of Alzheimer's. If this theory is correct, it means that as the disease advances and the patient moves into the middle and late stages of Alzheimer's, the effects of Cognex may lessen. (A physician can explain how and why Cognex affects early-stage and middle- and late-stage patients differently.) The important point for caregivers to remember is that there is no evidence that Cognex cures, or even alters, the underlying dementing process of Alzheimer's disease.

As with any medication, patients on Cognex therapy must be followed by a physician to monitor dosing closely. Patients also should watch carefully for signs of side effects. (The Notes section in the last chapter is a good place to keep records.)

We should measure affection
by its strength and constancy.
Cicero
(Roman statesman)

CHAPTER 4

Finances and the Law

The law is what it is—
a majestic edifice,
sheltering all of us,
each stone of which
rests on another.

John Galsworthy
(English novelist)

The financial issues surrounding Alzheimer's disease vary and should be considered carefully. Start by contacting your local chapter of the Alzheimer's Disease and Related Disorders Association (sometimes known as "ADRDA" or the "Alzheimer's Association"). It's in the phone book. The counselors there will confirm that there are three major areas to consider:

Information Gathering—anticipating your financial needs and reviewing your income and assets.

Learning How to Pay—covering medical and care expenses.

Legal Planning—preparing durable power of attorney, living wills, and healthcare proxies; dealing with guardianships, estate, and financial planning; and finding the right lawyer.

Planning

Financial and legal planning may require the services of a lawyer, but first you will need to review your income, assets, and expenses—so you can plan to meet your needs.

If You Have Been Living With the Patient with Alzheimer's

- Gather financial records from the last three years.
- Figure your average monthly expenses: housing, food, clothing, car/transportation, household help, etc *(information on how to anticipate these expenses is discussed in detail in the next section, "Paying for Care")*.
- Figure your average yearly expenses: taxes, insurance, medical bills, vacations, repairs, etc.

- Figure extraordinary expenses: medical, changes related to housing, etc. Calculate the additional expenses you may need to care for the patient over the next few years, including the cost of assistance you will need to pay for.
- Take a realistic look at what these additional expenses will do to your financial situation.

If the Patient is Moving Into Your Home

- Figure your family's expenses.
- Estimate the cost of adding a person to your home.
- Trim costs where you can.

If You are Moving in With the Patient

- Figure the patient's expenses.
- Estimate the cost of your entry into the household.

The person with Alzheimer's disease may not recall information about his or her income or assets or owing or being owed money. A look through old checks and papers may disclose leads to income and assets and IOUs; debts usually show up on their own. To keep track of bills, ask the post office to forward the patient's mail to you. If bills are lost and become overdue, call the company and make arrangements for payment.

Paying for Care

Anticipating Expenses

Ask yourself these questions: Will changes in housing be necessary? An additional room? An extra bathroom? The answers may involve guesswork, but thinking about these questions can still be helpful.

Consider what might be necessary: the cost of medication and outside services like visiting nurses, home care aides, transportation, the cost of meals, food, clothing, electricity, phone, legal, and accounting fees.

Even if an insurance plan seems to cover all medical expenses, many things are not covered: repairs to a wheelchair or hospital-style bed, cost of incontinence supplies, etc. They should all be estimated and counted into the larger picture.

Write it all down. Start now to keep track of all medically related expenses and to save all receipts—not just for estimating future expenses, but also for the IRS and to apply for public and/or community aid.

Most important, remember that Medicare and private health insurance—except for the newer long-term care policies—do not cover the costs of aides and companions in most cases.

Identifying Income and Assets

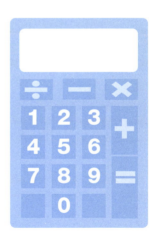

A person with Alzheimer's may either forget or become confused or secretive about income and assets. A careful look at these resources may show that there is more help available than you thought. Try to gather everything that looks helpful, including:

- Bank and other account statements
- Bank books
- Canceled checks
- Insurance policies and receipts
- Will and any trusts

- Business and legal papers
- Address books
- Credit cards and past statements
- Keys to desks, file cabinets, and safety deposit boxes
- Tax returns

Most Common Types of Income and Assets

Salaries. Keep in mind that continuing work may not be possible for you or the patient with Alzheimer's.

Pensions and Social Security. Record the patient's Social Security number and check with all past employers about pensions and disability insurance. Old resumes may help you find previous employers. Being a member of a union (in the past or in the present) or of the clergy may carry benefits. Check on military service benefits and services.

You will need some sort of proof of service or identification to show branch of service—dog tags, discharge papers, pictures, or old uniforms.

Jointly owned assets–Speak to your financial advisor about the benefits and possible liabilities of separate rather than joint accounts.

Annuities. These are common resources for many senior citizens.

Stocks, bonds, mutual funds. Check for certificates—even if they are very old and seem to be of no value—and look for statements and receipts.

Safety deposit box. Check also for evidence of a safety deposit box, such as a key or a canceled check or receipt for rent. But realize that you may not be allowed to get into the box without a court order.

Insurance policies. Make a list of issuing companies, the policy purpose (life, disability, health), and identification numbers of all policies. Check the patient's wallet to see if insurance cards have been issued. The patient's physician(s) may be helpful with policy numbers.

Does the patient have an accelerated benefits rider for the life insurance policies? This could be a payment source for long-term care.

Real estate. Is there any vacation property or vacant land somewhere?

Personal property. Include items such as automobiles, boats, collections, jewels, antiques, etc. One way to locate the existence and value of such items is through household or renter's insurance policies.

Families. Your family may be your biggest asset. Consider if and how family members might be called on to help. Those who live far away may be better able to give financial support than time. Get everyone involved.

Taxing matters–Consider using an accounting professional or CPA to get all the tax
benefits you are entitled to, including deduc-
tions for the care of a dependent Alzheimer's
patient. Also, the Internal Revenue Code
allows the elderly certain tax benefits. If you
or the patient are elderly, call your local IRS
office and ask for the booklet *Tax Benefits
for Older Americans.*

Meeting the High Cost of Alzheimer's Disease—Who Pays for What?[18]

Alzheimer's disease can be an expensive illness, but
there are some, though limited, federal, state, and
private resources available to help you
offset the costs—including social
work services, adult day-care centers,
recreation centers, respite programs,
and sheltered housing.

Medicare and Medicaid are the most
common sources of payment—after
family assets, voluntary agencies, and
insurance plans.

If you have been rejected by one agency for a particular expense, try another agency and then return to
the first agency to help meet other expenses.

Finance hotline–The US Department of Health
and Human Services maintains a hotline for
healthcare financing: 1-800-638-6833.

Medicare[18]

Medicare is a US government medical insurance program run by the Health Care Financing Administration and your local Social Security agency. The program covers persons who are more than age 65 and are eligible for Social Security or Railroad Retirement benefits. It also covers people under 65 who have received Social Security Disability for more than two years.

Medicare regulations are complex and change frequently; you will probably need professional help in obtaining all the benefits to which you are entitled.

Agencies that provide the services—the Home Health Care Agency or the Visiting Nurse Association, for example—will know which are reimbursable. *Caution:* these healthcare providers tend to be conservative about the extent of benefits available; you may need advice from a knowledgeable lawyer or Medicare advocacy organization.

As for home care, Medicare will cover some nursing home and home care costs ordered by a physician. But the amount of the benefit and the time period in which it can be used are limited and related to the patient's need for skilled care.

Medicare will pay for up to 100 days of post-hospital nursing home care provided the patient was hospitalized for at least three days and enters the nursing home within one month of the hospitalization. The first 20 days are paid in full by Medicare, and the patient is responsible for paying $84.80 a day for the next 80 days. But to be covered, the care the patient needs must be considered "skilled," and most Alzheimer's disease patients are considered as needing only "custodial care," which is not covered. Medicare pays for only 4% of all nursing home care costs in the nation today. Don't count on Medicare for nursing home costs in most cases. You may want to seek professional help to clarify the extent of Medicare coverage.

Home care benefits are also problematical. In theory the patient is entitled to up to 35 hours a week of "part-time and intermittent" home care if the patient is homebound. Here again the patient must need skilled care to obtain the home care benefit, and the application is usually turned down. But the home care agency that usually makes the initial determination may be wrong, and care can be obtained with some help from a knowledgeable lawyer or not-for-profit advocacy groups such as the Legal Assistance for Medicare Patients (LAMP) in Connecticut or the Medicare Beneficiaries Defense Fund in New York.

If your request for reimbursement is at first rejected by Medicare, you can always ask that the decision be reviewed. But there are strict time limits to appeal, so you may want to talk to a lawyer.

Medicaid[18]

Medicaid is a joint federal and state government insurance program run by the states. Assistance is furnished on the basis of need. Apply through the local branch (usually a county office) of the agency that administers the program in your state—the Department of Social Services, the Department of Welfare, or the Health Department.

Qualifying for Medicaid

Qualification for Medicaid is means "tested" and depends on the income and assets, in addition to the medical and personal needs, of the patient. The eligibility requirements differ from state to state. *In general, the patient may have very limited assets.* Assets that are "transferred" as a gift three years or more before application for Medicaid or have been "spent down" are not counted, but gifts made within three years of application will cause a waiting period, except for certain allowable transfers to a spouse or disabled or blind child.

To "spend down," the patient must spend his or her money and get "fair value" for it. Expenses for the needs of the patient or spouse are allowable, of course, and certain assets are "exempt" (not countable). For example, the patient may purchase a home, and the home is exempt as long as the patient, the spouse, or a minor or blind or disabled child resides there. Other exempt assets include some furniture, life insurance, burial funds and a burial plot, and a family car. But a gift of money (to children, for example) cannot be used to bring down total assets. Be sure to talk to a lawyer or accountant for clarity about this subject—it's very important. A new Medicaid law was passed by Congress in August of 1993, and the changes enacted significantly affect the necessary planning.

To determine your eligibility for Medicaid, you may wish to ask for information about the Medicaid program (technically known as "Medical Assistance" and in California as "MediCal") from the state agency that runs the program and the state or local Agency on Aging. Be careful. Medicaid is extremely technical and ever-changing. Government workers may be incorrect about the information they give or may provide restrictive interpretations of the law. The local ADRDA chapter is a good source of information about Medicaid and will frequently have seminars and workshops about the program. The local chapters will also have referral lists of knowledgeable elder law attorneys in the community.

If the patient is eligible for Medicaid, it will cover nursing home costs regardless of whether the patient's care is defined as skilled or custodial. Medicaid pays the nursing home directly. If the patient's income is allocated to the spouse, the spouse handles payment to the nursing home.

Spouses of nursing home patients who receive Medicaid benefits have certain financial protection. These rights vary from state to state but involve a monthly income allowance and a resource allowance to assure the "at-home" spouse a certain amount of assets and a minimum monthly income out of the couple's total income and assets. State rules vary dramatically, but if a lawyer expert in Medicaid law is consulted, it may be possible to obtain benefits for the at-home spouse greater than the state's minimums.

A few states have a Medicaid home care program. If your state does, it will pay for personal care at home even if the patient's needs are deemed not to be skilled. The amount of care will depend on the patient's individual needs and the extent of the state's program.

As this manual goes to print, President Clinton is preparing his health cost reform proposals. Very preliminary press reports indicate some new home- and community-based services may be proposed to the Congress.

Legal Arrangements

Although primarily a medical problem, caring for an Alzheimer's disease patient has a lot to do with the law. This section will cover some of the most important legal issues facing the Alzheimer's patient and caregiver. An elder law attorney will probably be necessary. Laws vary from state to state and they are changing rapidly, often in response to the needs and demands of an increasingly larger and better organized population.

The Elder Law Attorney

"Elder law" is the name given to the field of law that deals with issues of aging, incapacity, planning for dealing with serious illness and long-term care, government benefit programs, protective services, guardianship, and tax and estate planning.

Elder law attorneys do estate planning and prepare living wills and durable powers of attorney. They can unravel the complexities of Medicare,

Medicaid, and public benefits, and they are well-versed in issues such as age discrimination and patients' rights.

There are some general issues that need to be evaluated at the outset. Because one goal should be to, as much as possible, let patients maintain their own decision-making about their own affairs, the patient's ability to make sound decisions should be evaluated. The physician working with the lawyer, social worker, patient, and family can help make this evaluation. Of course, patients' awareness of their condition is the key factor. If patients are not aware that they have a medical problem, or if they do not understand the nature of their medical condition, they may be reluctant to plan anything.

Unless there is a clear inability to make decisions, the patient can and should participate in the planning to the maximum extent possible.

To find an attorney in your community who specializes in elder law, write to the National Academy of Elder Law Attorneys, Inc, 655 N Alvernon, Suite 108, Tucson, Arizona 85771, or call 602-881-4005 and request its *Experience Registry.* NAELA can provide a pamphlet about choosing an attorney, as well as pamphlets about many other subjects.

Ethical Issues

No matter how close and loving a family may be, some of the actions that may need to be taken to protect the patient—and the spouse or other family members—may raise legal and ethical conflicts of interest. These potential conflicts increase as the patient's incapacity grows. What are the patient's wishes about Medicaid planning, which may involve gifting assets to the spouse? Is this what the patient would want, or would he or she expect the resources to be spent only on his or her own care? Who would the patient choose as a spokesperson when communication is no longer possible? To make decisions? Investments? Planning? Healthcare decisions? Are the interests, needs, and burdens of other family members so great that they cannot honestly do what is right for the patient? Can the lawyer the family visits adequately and fairly represent all family members?

Lawyers and ethicists are struggling with these very issues. The answers are not clear. All the caregiver can do is be aware that such conflicts exist and try hard to do what is fair to all parties concerned. Remember, patients and families have different needs, all of which may be legitimate, and a way needs to be found to reach a fair and reasonable solution in each case. Counselors at your local ADRDA chapter, social workers, and elder law attorneys are trained to recognize and deal with these issues.

Patient and Financial Management

We should all plan to protect ourselves against the possibility of becoming incapacitated in later life. This can be done by taking certain planning actions such as the ones described below. If a person has not taken these steps before an illness is diagnosed, it still may not be too late to develop protection. As a caregiver, you can really help a patient who has not planned properly. Let's look at some of the things that should be done.

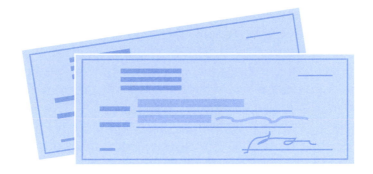

Financial Management Systems

It is important to set up a system to manage the patient's financial affairs if the time comes when the patient cannot act on his or her own. The basic tools to do this are the *durable power of attorney* and *the living trust.*

Durable power of attorney (DPA). A durable power of attorney is a written delegation of authority to another person or persons to act as the "agent" of the incapacitated person when assistance by another is needed. A DPA can be limited to a few tasks or it can be broad, in which case it is called a "general" power of attorney. "Durable" means the agent can act even though the maker of the power of attorney is incapacitated; such a power remains in effect when illness strikes. It is very important to have wording in the document that says it is valid even if disability occurs.

Most states have forms set out in the state's statutes that can be used, but it is better to consult a lawyer so that the power of attorney can be tailored to your specific needs. Even though signing the general "statutory" form should be sufficient, many banks and other financial institutions do not like the statutory forms and want their own; it is probably a good idea to take the trouble to sign them as well.

Living trust. A living trust is a more formal type of management system and a good one for many persons. A trust is a contract (the "trust agreement") between a person who owns property (securities, cash accounts, real estate, for example), sometimes called the "donor," or "grantor," and a person selected to manage that property (the "trustee"). The trustee agrees to hold the property transferred to the trust for the benefit of the donor in accordance with the rules set out in the trust agreement. The trust will specify how the trust funds are to be spent and what happens to these funds when the donor dies.

The living trust is an excellent vehicle for property management, and when a person's means are sizable it is generally more effective than the power of attorney, although both should be executed.

Joint bank accounts. Joint bank accounts can be managed by either co-owner and thus are an effective management system for those accounts, because, under the banking laws of most states, either co-owner has free access to all the joint account funds. But this is not true with other kinds of jointly owned assets; one co-owner of jointly owned stocks, for example, cannot sell or transfer those shares without the signature of the co-owner.

Healthcare Decisions

Having the tools to make healthcare decisions for a patient who can no longer decide is just as important as having property management authority. First, remember that it is the patient's wishes that are paramount. Every one of us has the right to make our own healthcare decisions, and physicians, hospitals, and nursing homes have a legal and ethical obligation to consult with us, listen to us, and follow our wishes, without imposing their values and ideas on us.

But what happens if we can no longer speak for ourselves? Certainly we do not lose our right to decide, but if our wishes are not known, they may not be carried out. Others may make decisions for us that we would not have wanted.

The best way to ensure that our wishes are known and respected is to sign, in advance, papers that express these wishes. The two basic documents designed to accomplish this are the *living will* and *the healthcare proxy* (sometimes called a "healthcare power of attorney").

Living will. A living will is a document that expresses the person's wishes as to the healthcare that person wishes to have in the event of a serious illness from which there is no reasonable hope of recovery. This document is to be used when that person can no longer communicate his or her wishes.

Healthcare proxy. The *healthcare proxy* is a document whereby the person delegates to a *healthcare agent* the power to make healthcare decisions in accordance with that person's wishes as expressed in the written living will (or otherwise) when the patient can no longer communicate those wishes. An alternate healthcare agent should be nominated. In some states the living will and the proxy may be combined into one document.

The laws regarding powers of attorney, trusts, living wills, and healthcare proxies vary greatly from state to state and are constantly in flux. An attorney or advocacy organization (such as Choice In Dying, Inc, 200 Varick Street, New York, NY 10014) may need to be consulted for this kind of planning.

No Advance Planning?

If the patient did not plan ahead and there are no property management systems in place, it will probably be necessary to apply to the state court for the appointment of a *guardian* for property management and personal care decisions (in some states such a person is called a *conservator).* In most cases this is less desirable than having a power of attorney or trust in effect, and the procedure to have a guardian appointed is often time consuming and expensive. Further, the court may appoint a person as guardian who would not have been the choice of the patient. It is much better to do the advance planning.

Don't forget that both the patient and the patient's spouse should have a will, and if wills have been signed they should be reviewed. If the spouse of the patient were to die first, that spouse's funds should be left in trust for the benefit of the surviving spouse who is ill. Like all of the legal and financial issues discussed here, this should be discussed with your lawyer.

The greatest pleasure I know is to do a good action.

Charles Lamb
(English writer)

Further Reading

Guide to Health Insurance for People with Medicare. US Department of Health and Human Services. Health Care Financing Administration, Baltimore, Maryland 21207. (Ask for publication No. HCFA-02110 and a catalogue of related material.)

National Academy of Elder Law Attorneys, Inc, 655 N Alvernon, Suite 108, Tucson, Arizona 85771 (602-881-4005).

Resource Directory for Older People: A directory of more than 200 organizations that provide legal, health, and consumer information for the elderly. Available from the Superintendent of Documents, US Government Printing Office, Washington, DC 20402 ($10).

Safe
Home

CHAPTER 5

Home Safe Home

*Nothing's as good as
holding on to safety.*

Euripides
(Greek playwright)

Some of the symptoms of Alzheimer's disease—forgetfulness, confusion, and the need to pace or wander—make it necessary to take a new look around you. You'll want to make sure your patient is safe in and around the home and that the entire family has as little environmentally related stress as possible.

But you don't need to completely redo the house or lock up everything in sight. Complete change isn't necessary, and it might even be harmful. Drastic changes may very well confuse or agitate the Alzheimer's patient.

Get a first aid kit. Accidents happen in even the safest of homes. Ask your pharmacist/ nurse what to keep in a home first aid kit. The pharmacy may even sell first aid kits that are already fully supplied. Make sure the items are always handy, not outdated, and that you know how to use them.

Basic Concepts to Keep in Mind

Don't change too much. Change only what is necessary for safety, comfort, and the reduction of stress. If, for example, the patient is used to making morning toast and is still able to do so, changing the toaster for a new, "safer" type may distress the patient and may make it necessary for you to make breakfast all the time.

Make changes over time, as they are needed. Keep the stages of Alzheimer's in mind. In the early stages, when only mild confusion and forgetfulness are present, there may be little need to lock up all knives, and removing locks from doors may be unnecessary, even insulting. (Later it may be lifesaving!)

Make changes that simplify. Clutter confuses and may be dangerous. Objects on stairs can be tripped over. Wax fruit on a table may be taken for real. A pile of newspaper may be seen as a chair by someone with Alzheimer's.

Make changes that make life easier for you. Alzheimer's patients often wander, picking up items as they go, putting them down in other places or pocketing them. You may want to have out-of-reach, out-of-sight places for keys, handbags, or beloved breakables.

Kitchen and Bathroom Checklist

The bathroom and kitchen are by far the most dangerous places in the home. This list could help build your awareness of dangers you never have noticed. Checking them off should give you some peace of mind.

- ❏ Stove turned off by a valve or electric outlet at night
- ❏ Protective covers on stove knobs, or knobs removed from burners on a gas stove

- ☐ Radiators covered
- ☐ Matches and lighters put away
- ☐ Electrical equipment and kitchen equipment such as food processors and toasters unplugged at night. If necessary, fuses, circuit-breakers, or timers used to keep equipment safe at night
- ☐ Water temperature turned down to prevent burns
- ☐ Hot-water faucets painted red to minimize confusion
- ☐ Lock removed from inside bathroom door
- ☐ Loaded fire extinguisher handy in the kitchen
- ☐ Smoke detectors in working order
- ☐ Fire escape routes from the house cleared
- ☐ Weapons removed
- ☐ Potentially poisonous cleaners locked up

Safe Inside the House

The easiest way to handle the huge task of safe-proofing your home is item by item, room by room. You will discover your own list of necessary changes as you go.

Lighting. Make sure there is adequate lighting throughout the house, especially for nighttime trips from bed to bathroom, and at the top and bottom of stairs. Light the entranceway to the house. Avoid lighting that casts shadows on the wall at night. Use shades at night to block any incoming light from cars.

Stairs. Clear the clutter. Paint or mark the top and bottom steps and make sure railings are solid. You might want gates at the top and bottom of stairs. Lock the cellar doors and consider alarms or sensors that sound at all exits.

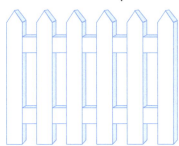

Mirrors. Consider covering all mirrors. Alzheimer's patients sometimes become afraid or confused by their own image in mirrors.

Floors. Remove or tightly fasten small rugs or carpets. Bathroom mats should have suction cups, and there should be nonslip strips in the tub and shower. Don't use a high-gloss wax on floors. Keep electric and phone cords out of the traffic path.

NOTE: **The danger of falls increases as Alzheimer's affects the areas of the brain that control muscles and coordination.**

> **When do accidents occur? Accidents happen when you are under stress, tired, irritated, or in a hurry. If you find that you're dropping or losing things and that the patient is getting upset—slow down, rest a bit, and let both of you calm down. It's better to be safe than on time.**

Windows. As confusion increases, lock windows and/or provide window guards.

Furniture. Arrange furniture with clear pathways. The furniture should be firm, not wobbly—if individual pieces have wheels, use plastic pads under them to stop unwanted rolling. Install safety bars in the bathroom, hallways, and other places where there may be danger of losing one's balance. If the patient has been bumping into edges of mantelpieces, doorways, or stairs, reflector tape from the local hardware store may help. It also may be a good idea to put padding on the sharp corners of furniture.

A room of your own? If at all possible, leave a room for yourself—someplace you can go and think and be with your favorite things without worry or concern.

Clothing. Put rubber soles and heels on shoes. Make sure hems are not torn or trailing and that sashes, sleeves, and scarves cannot get caught. Shoes should lace up or be fastened with Velcro™.

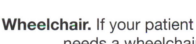

Walkers. Some patients can't learn to use new aids, but you might consider the use of a cane, walker, or "walker belt"—ask your doctor.

Wheelchair. If your patient needs a wheelchair, check that it's the right size to fit through the doorways of your home before you buy or rent. A wheelchair should have a small turning capacity and be light enough for you to handle during travel.

The number of the poison control center should be next to every phone in the house, along with the physician's name and phone number, the police, fire department, etc.

Cleaning supplies. As the patient loses the ability to read, there is increased danger of poisoning from eating or drinking cleaning supplies. Keep supplies in their original containers. Lock away poisonous supplies or keep them where they cannot be reached easily.

Medications. Make sure pills are clearly marked and that there is a regular system for taking the medications. Later, you may need to remove medicines from their usual storage place and bring them out only as needed.

Plants. Some household plants and bulbs are poisonous: dieffenbachia, poinsettia, holly (the red berries of the female plant), to name a few. Get a list from your florist or from the poison control center.

Swallowing dangerous objects. Remove or fasten down objects that are small enough to be put in the mouth or swallowed—decorative items such as marbles or beads, finials on lamps that could be unscrewed, bottle caps, loose keys and coins, etc.

Locks on doors. Additional locks placed very high or very low on your outside doors may help keep an Alzheimer's patient from wandering out of the house.

Holiday decorations. Check that your holiday decor is as safe as anything else in the house. You may want to simplify it as well. Decorating the whole house may be confusing for a person with

Alzheimer's because it drastically changes the environment.

Sharp objects. As the ability to remember the function of tools or control their use diminishes, patients need to be protected from sharp objects—including razor blades, knives, power tools, scissors, pins, needles, pencils, letter openers, and breakables such as glasses, dishes, lamps, and framed pictures on tables.

Water taps. As the patient becomes more forgetful, you may want to fasten taps so that they either turn off automatically or cannot be turned on by the patient. This will reduce the danger of a flood.

Spilled water. Alzheimer's patients may spill water and forget or be unable to wipe it up, and then they may slip and fall. Watch out for spills and keep the floor dry.

> **In the event of a fall: If you suspect a fracture, bad sprain, or head injury, do not move the patient. Keep him or her warm and comfortable. Call your local emergency telephone number or your physician. Do not panic.**

Safe Outside the House

It's almost impossible to think of everything you can do to ensure your patient's safety outside, but as long as the basic safety guidelines are followed, you can feel somewhat at ease. The key to safety outside is to let your neighbors and local authorities know the situation—that way, you are all on the alert.

The yard. The patient needs to be protected from wandering—into the street or neighboring yards. You can provide this protection by supervising the person, or you can use fences and gates to protect the patient. Be sure that dangerous objects in the yard, including clothes lines and barbecues, have been put away or made safe.

Walkways. Make sure the footing on walkways is safe and kept cleared of toys, lawnmowers, fallen branches, and thrown newspapers.

The garage. Keep the garage locked. Clearing it of dangerous objects is almost impossible.

Swimming pools, hot tubs, ornamental pools. Drowning can occur in a very small amount of water. Be sure to drain or reduce the danger of all standing water. Keep all pool areas enclosed and locked.

In case of emergency. Carry a list of *all* medicines taken by the patient. Include phone numbers of the pharmacy, the physician, and the poison control center. This information is helpful to a physician at an emergency room and can save time for the regular physician as well. The patient should carry a duplicate list and wear an identification bracelet with his or her name on it. A Medic-Alert bracelet is linked with a 24-hour telephone hotline.

Driving. Driving may be dangerous for a person with Alzheimer's. The patient who is used to driving, however, is often reluctant to give up the keys, even when the necessity becomes obvious to others. If reasoning doesn't work, you may have to resort to hiding keys or keeping the car locked in the garage. (These measures will be necessary only until the patient loses interest in driving.)

In the car. Seat belts are important. They keep the patient safe and prevent interference with the driver. The back seat with a seat belt is the safest place for the pas-senger with

Alzheimer's. Lock the door to prevent the patient from getting out of the car while it's moving.

In someone else's car. Many patients with Alzheimer's are frightened of getting into strange vehicles, including city buses and the vans that take them to day care.

Backing the patient into the vehicle is sometimes helpful. Make sure all vehicles in which the patient travels are safely maintained and have usable seat belts.

Objects that often litter a car should be cleared away—windshield cleaner, old cigarettes, coins, and pencils can pose a danger. Windows and door handles or buttons the patient can play with should be taped to prevent accidents.

> *Charity and personal force*
> *are the only investments worth anything.*
>
> Walt Whitman
> (American poet)

Further Reading

The Caring Home Booklet from the Andrus Gerontology Center, Program in Policy and Services Research, University of Southern California, Los Angeles, CA 90089-0191.

Raschko B. *Housing Interiors for the Disabled and Elderly.* New York: Van Nostrand Reinhold, 1984.

Ronch J. *Alzheimer's Disease: A Practical Guide for Those Who Help Others.* New York: Cross and Continuum, 1989.

Day
to Day

CHAPTER 6

Day to Day

*My candle burns
at both ends;
it will not
last the night;
but ah, my foes,
and oh, my friends;
it gives a lovely light.*

Edna St. Vincent Millay
(American poet)

People with Alzheimer's disease can continue carrying out most of their daily needs for quite a while after the onset of the illness. As their abilities inevitably decline, however, you will need to give them more and more help.

This can be an ordeal. Knowing a few basics can help. The following suggestions about dressing, eating, bathing, grooming, toileting, recreation, sleep, and communication can save you time, frustration, and despair.

The longer the person with Alzheimer's uses all possible mental and physical capacities, the longer a higher quality of life can be continued. Helping the patient with Alzheimers promotes feelings of independence, self-respect, and control. Helping, not doing. This is important because, though often childlike, the patient is an adult who should not be infantilized or made to feel overly dependent.

Helping, Not Doing

Bathing

Bathing is such a well-learned habit that most patients with Alzheimer's are able to manage by themselves far into their illness.

Keep it simple. Have bathing be a regular routine, done at the same time of day, in the same steps. Some caregivers have the patient bathe fully every day, but that may not be necessary. Every other day or every third day may be adequate. Use your judgment—sometimes a cloth bath may suffice, especially if the patient is anxious or fearful.

Many patients prefer a shower to a bath—it's easier and feels safer. If you use a tub, put only about six inches of water in and stay with the patient. It's helpful if the patient is in the room, and preferably in the tub, as the tub fills with water. Sometimes patients are startled or become agitated when they enter a tub without having seen it being filled.

Stay calm and take it step by step. A bath may take all morning—in fact, it may be the only thing you do today! This is not your fault. Keep these guidelines in mind when bathing the patient. Remember that if only the important parts get washed, the bath is a success.

Don't use slippery oils or bubble bath.

Provide support—handrails, a bench, nonslip strips, etc.

Wash in the same order every time.

Wash genitals thoroughly—sponges or mitts may help. This area needs to be kept clean, even if it's the only area you clean that day.

Some patients in the early stages enjoy playing in the tub. If you put a comfortable chair in the bathroom, their play time may give you time to read or relax.

Help the patient dry in the same order he or she washes. Use powder, body lotion, or skin cream to prevent rashes—skin on older people often needs extra protection.

Grooming

Good grooming helps patients feel better about themselves. It also helps the caregiver. It's much more pleasant to live with someone who is up and dressed and nicely groomed each day than with someone who mopes around unshaven or untidy.

Hair. Keep hair in an easy-to-care-for style. Washing hair at the kitchen sink may be easier than in the tub or shower. Get a hose/spray attachment to make rinsing easier.

If the barber shop or beauty parlor has been an important part of the patient's former routine, you might want to continue having the patient go to the same place and the same person. Later, you may find a service willing to come to you.

Shaving. It may be difficult for you to shave the patient, so try to supervise shaving for the time being. Later, an electric razor may simplify the job for you and the patient. In addition to helping female patients shave their legs and underarms, you may need to help women who have facial hair either pluck or shave their chins.

Praise after shaving—"See how nice you look!"—may help the patient feel good about the effort.

Make-up. Most female patients stop using make-up early in the disease. But a woman who has always worn make-up will feel better about herself if she continues using it. Light-tone lipstick and a bit of powder should be enough. Eye make-up is too hard.

NOTE: **Patients may be frightened by their reflection in a mirror or not recognize themselves—in that case, cover the mirrors.**

Nails. Encourage your patient to continue trimming fingernails and toenails. When you finally take over, do it about twice a month. (You may get more co-operation if you do it while the patient is watching television or listening to music.)

Difficulty with toenails, bunions, or calluses may cause discomfort or problems with walking. A visit to a podiatrist every six months or so might be helpful and may be covered by insurance. Check the patient periodically to make sure shoes fit properly, especially if you notice the patient has gained or lost weight.

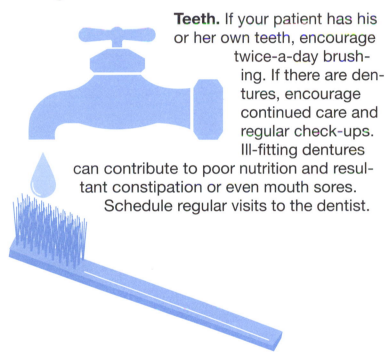

Teeth. If your patient has his or her own teeth, encourage twice-a-day brushing. If there are dentures, encourage continued care and regular check-ups. Ill-fitting dentures can contribute to poor nutrition and resultant constipation or even mouth sores. Schedule regular visits to the dentist.

The goal is continued independence. When Alzheimer's patients start to forget daily grooming tasks, don't perform these tasks for them—remind them of what comes next.

Toileting

Special attention must be paid to ensure the toileting experience is comfortable, safe, and hygienic. It's a good idea to check frequently if the patient needs to use the toilet.

Most people with Alzheimer's disease are able to use the toilet on their own through the early stages of the illness. As time goes on, more help is needed: help to remove clothing, to sit on the toilet, to flush, and to clean properly. Always ask permission to help—that helps patients maintain a sense of control.

Simplifying the process. Prevent accidents by making it easy to find the bathroom. A picture of a toilet on the bathroom door or bright-colored paint on the door may help remind the patient where the bathroom is.

A night-light or reflective tape on the bathroom door may help the patient get there. Loose-fitting, easy-to-remove underclothing will lessen the likelihood of accidents.

Respecting your patient's privacy, while ensuring safety, will encourage continued and independent use of the toilet.

Learn to recognize the nonverbal cues the patient gives about needing the toilet; respond to them quickly.

Constipation. Poor diet and inactivity can cause constipation. So can some medications. Ask advice from your physician. Regular activity, like a daily walk, is essential. Make sure the patient has adequate amounts of fiber in the diet. Consult your physician about laxatives and/or stool softeners if increased exercise does not seem to be working.

Drink plenty of liquids. This is important to maintain adequate hydration and help prevent constipation. Make sure the patient in your care drinks five to eight glasses of water, tea, mineral water, or juice every day.

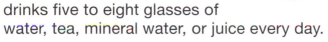

Urinary incontinence. Make sure the patient sees a doctor to determine if urinary incontinence is due to Alzheimer's disease. Urinary incontinence can sometimes be managed by recognizing the cues the patient gives when he needs to use the bathroom. Many caregivers find it helpful to put the patient on a schedule for toileting—for example, having the patient use the bathroom every two to three hours. Urinary incontinence can also be coped with by using adult absorbency pads. Covering these pads with regular underwear can help the patient feel less childlike. Pads should be changed frequently and skin washed thoroughly to avoid odor and skin rashes. Be sure to consult your doctor about the problem, so that urinary tract infection can be ruled out as a cause of the incontinence.

Nighttime incontinence can be lessened by withholding fluids at night and by using a pad. Sometimes medication can help—talk to the patient's doctor.

Bowel incontinence. When bowel incontinence develops in patients with Alzheimer's disease, it's usually at the later stages of the disease. First, make sure the patient's bowel incontinence isn't due to fecal impaction or drug side effects. Bowel incontinence is almost never reversible once it starts. Protective pants can be used with absorbency pads.[14] Protective bed padding may also be needed. Keep in mind, too, that it's possible to manage the patient's bowel incontinence by monitoring diet. Learn the patient's bowel regimen and lengthen toileting at that time.

Cleanliness is the goal. To avoid serious skin problems, daily bathing and a regular change of clothes are essential.

Dressing

Patients with Alzheimer's should continue dressing themselves as long as possible. To help, simplify their clothing, clothing care, storage, and dressing procedures.

Simplify clothing. Clothing should be easy to put on, wear, and remove—with large front fastenings, zippers, and Velcro™ tabs. Over-the-head, loose-fitting clothing, elastic waistbands, wraparounds, and reversible fabric really help.

Underpants should be soft and loosely constructed. A bra may not be necessary for a woman with Alzheimer's—try using an undershirt or a T-shirt instead. (Keep in mind, a woman who has worn a bra all her life may feel demeaned by being suddenly without one.)

Shoes should lace up or be fastened with Velcro™.

Tube socks are best. Avoid tight socks or stockings that can impair circulation.

Clothing Care

Keep clothing up to date, clean, color coordinated, and neat.

Use comfortable fabrics like cotton rather than wool. As clothes wear out, replace them with machine washable, unrestrictive, no-iron items.

If the patient prefers wearing the same shirt or dress over and over, buy duplicates.

Suggest to family and friends the clothing design, color, and fabric that is most useful as a gift—unless they've helped a person with Alzheimer's dress, they'll have no idea what works.

Storage

The patient should be able to reach clothes in the closet and dresser drawers easily. Sort and arrange all clothing by type: hang all skirts together, all pants, all shirts. In the drawers, keep all socks together, all underpants, all night-wear.

Hangers that serve the same purpose should have the same design. All pants or skirt hangers, for example, should either have clips or a pressure bar.

Put out-of-season clothes away.

Put ties, scarves, belts or sashes, and other accessories with the item of clothing they go with. As you find that a particular item causes confusion, adapt it or eliminate it. If a woman, for example, forgets how to tie a scarf—fasten it to her dress already tied or remove it altogether.

Dressing Procedures

To reduce the danger of falls, have the patient dress while seated; stand close to provide support.

Ask, "Do you want to wear the *red* or the *green?*" But do not offer too many choices—it's confusing. Speaking positively helps—"Red looks really nice on you!"

Check to make sure all fastenings are closed and that clothing is appropriate before going out. As time passes, it may become necessary to lay out the next day's clothing at night—but not necessarily in the patient's room or within easy reach. If you do lay out clothing, do so in the order in which it is put on.

Glasses

Make sure that you have more than one pair available for the person with Alzheimer's and that you have a copy of the prescription. Choose plastic lenses rather than glass.

Neck cords may make searching for glasses unnecessary, but be aware that the cord could catch on something and present safety problems.

Eating

Dinner time can be the best of times or the worst of times, depending on your expectations and your preparedness. The following suggestions may help.

Planning and preparing meals. The appetite of the patient with Alzheimer's will vary from extremely hungry to simply not hungry at all. When appetites are too big to be healthful, serve just the right amount on a plate and remove other food from view.

The patient with Alzheimer's might be able to help with preparing a meal. Try a simple task like peeling potatoes or setting the table. Be wary of letting the patient use the stove.

Serve favorite foods often, especially if the patient has little appetite. Variety doesn't matter so long as the day's intake is well-balanced. Cook food the way the patient likes it—even though it may not be the way you like it.

Use contrasting colors of dishware and tablecloth/place mats. This helps the patient better identify plates, cups, silverware.

Add extra nutrients to the diet of a patient who eats too little; wheat germ can be added to soups, shredded carrots to tuna fish, and grated lemon to salads. Add powdered skim milk to milk shakes for extra protein. Five small meals a day may be easier to handle than three large ones. Nutritional supplements may also provide extra nutrients. Ask the doctor which supplements are best.

Spoons are easier than forks. And finger foods are easier still. If food needs cutting, cut it in the kitchen before bringing it to the table, to avoid difficulty or embarrassment.

Eat together. Eating with others keeps the patient with Alzheimer's more sociable, better nourished, and less likely to withdraw.

Keep finger foods available in the refrigerator for snacks, as this encourages the patient to eat.

Observe the patient's food intake carefully. If it's insufficient, offer a nutritious snack about an hour later.

Helping at Meal Time

Do not try to serve or feed a person who is upset or sleepy.

Be organized and stay calm.

Use a plastic tablecloth or place mats, straws, non-spill cups, and dishware with suction cups.

If the patient has dentures, make sure they are in place.

A bib or special "meal-time" shirt will reduce the need to change and wash clothing.

Check temperatures to make sure foods are not too hot.

If the patient is not eating, try this: get his or her attention, take a piece of food from your plate, and put the food in your mouth while looking at the patient. Then say, "It's your turn."

People with Alzheimer's often like sweet foods and fruit. Keep a dish of fruit available.

Serve foods that don't need much chewing: soups, ground meat, mashed potatoes, applesauce, pureed vegetables. Baby foods are fine, but expensive; try a food processor or a table grinder.

Keep the presentation of the food simple. If it's too confusing for the patient, offer one item at a time.

As the patient's condition gets worse, keep in mind that you do not *have* to eat with the patient. If eating with the patient makes you uncomfortable and you want to eat separately, that's okay.

Eating together goes a long way toward preserving an atmosphere of love and connection in the house! There will be times, however, when a sit-down meal won't work. In that case, enjoy your own meal and let the patient eat what he or she likes.

Feeding the Bed-Bound Patient

Protect sheets with a plastic cover placed under the food tray.

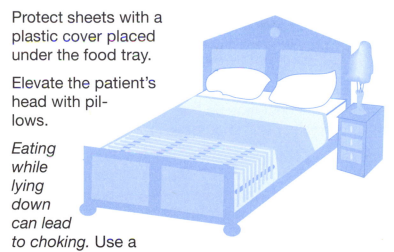

Elevate the patient's head with pillows.

Eating while lying down can lead to choking. Use a bendable straw or drinking tube for liquids. Keep the sipping end of the straw above the level of the liquid, and always support the patient's head.

Encourage the patient to help—for example, the patient could hold a straw, guide a cup, or reach for a spoon. Let patients do as much as they can for as long as they can.

Serve lukewarm foods that need little chewing.

Feed from a half-full spoon. Leave five seconds or so before offering more food.

A Choking Emergency?

Ask your physician or the Red Cross to teach you a method of clearing the airway of a choking person, such as the Heimlich maneuver.

Eating Out

Eat out occasionally. Excess or loud noise can disturb a patient with Alzheimer's, so avoid the peak eating hours and try to find a quiet restaurant. You may need to order for the patient. Offer the patient a choice of two things; tell the waiter quietly that your companion is confused and not able to answer questions, and remove extra glassware, silver, and condiments from reach.

Consider restaurant carry-out or delivery services—the cost may be less than the emotional cost of cooking meal after meal.

When eating out is no longer possible, there may be services in your community that provide meals for older persons in recreation centers or churches. Some may even provide transportation.

Recreation

Although a regular routine is generally best for the person with Alzheimer's disease, don't forget FUN. Recreation can be watching TV, walking, visiting friends, looking through magazines, going to religious services—whatever suits the individual. If one activity is refused, try another. For TV watching or radio listening, try to choose programs the patient has enjoyed in the past, programs from the patient's generation—for example, reruns of The Lawrence Welk Show or MASH.

NOTE: **Be aware that watching TV may confuse and disturb some patients with Alzheimer's. They may think the people on TV are in the room. If so,**

eliminate television. Music can be a satisfying substitute.

Suggested Recreational Activities

Looking at photos in a family album and identifying individuals, when possible, can be a valuable exercise.

Music and free-form dancing can be fun for everyone.

Tasks like arranging flatware in a drawer, piling newspapers in a box, folding clothes, stuffing Christmas cards, or sorting coins are productive and can be enjoyable for the patient.

Playing, petting, and interacting with pets can be rewarding.

Walking the dog is good exercise. Keep an eye on the leash, though, because it's easy to trip over it.

Watering and caring for plants is often satisfying. Sorting floral arrangements can also be an option.

Patients with Alzheimer's can participate with young children—coloring and playing games with no loss of dignity. Children usually don't have rigid ideas about what is and what is not appropriate behavior for adults.

Arts and crafts materials can be interesting—drawing, painting, cutting, pasting, and tracing are all satisfying pastimes.

The patient with Alzheimer's is often happy to help with kitchen and garden tasks, even housework. Choose the task with an eye toward safety.

Sleeping

Keep the room's lighting at maximum level, but close the drapes to avoid shadows.

Sundowning. People with Alzheimer's disease experience restlessness and the desire to wander or pace. This activity is called "sundowning," and it occurs in the late afternoon. It may be related to lack of light or to the increased home activity that occurs in the late afternoon and evening. When sundowning occurs, try to provide activity for the patient, because if there is nothing to do, sundowning can persist for a long time.

If possible, provide a quiet space for your patient. Perhaps late afternoon could be a time for listening to music or watching TV. Make the area as safe as possible, and let the pacing and muttering begin!

Sleeping arrangements. The person with Alzheimer's disease is often sleepless. A walk or ride in the car or a snack just before bedtime may help create sleepiness.

Room temperature and bedding should be comfortable. A washable quilt is easier than sheets and a blanket. Night-lights are invaluable.

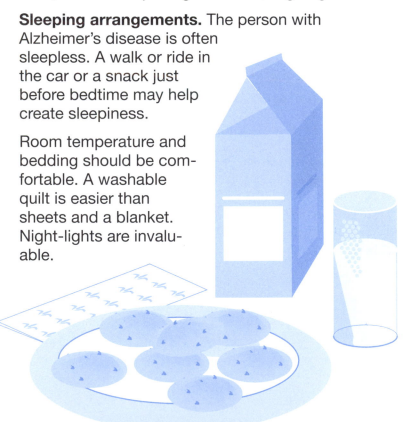

Speak softly to patients with Alzheimer's, especially when they wake in the middle of the night. Patients may get up, wander, and fall asleep in another room. There is no stopping them, so you might as well relax and let it happen—as long as the house is checked for safety.

Communications

A person with Alzheimer's disease passes through different stages of communication loss. Recognizing those stages may help you know what you can expect next—you may be able to find ways to communicate at each level.

Stage One—Slight Communication Loss

Words and events may be forgotten at this stage. (Don't take it personally if birthdays, happy times, even people are forgotten.)

There are long pauses between words and sentences. (Don't fill in the blanks or talk for him or her. Be patient.)

Forgotten words may be replaced with different words. (Learn the new language.)

The patient will try to hide the communication problem with a joke. (Laughing is fine, but don't make fun. Encourage continuing communications by accepting those that are possible.)

The patient may lose track or ramble. (Don't interrupt.)

The patient's understanding at this stage is related to a decreasing attention span. (Be brief and to the point. Don't talk longer than the patient's attention can last.)

An important point to remember is that patients with Alzheimer's pick up easily on a caregiver's mood. Be aware of how your mood could affect the patient while you're communicating.

---

10 STEPS TO IMPROVED COMMUNICATION

1. Get the patient's attention.
2. Speak clearly, in short, direct sentences—use one-step commands.
3. Be willing to repeat and rephrase.
4. Don't use slang.
5. Keep your tone warm and empathetic.
6. Ask simple questions.
7. Avoid baby talk.
8. Avoid pronouns—use names for clarity.
9. Write big, clear messages and post them.
10. Praise and encourage your patient; show affection.

Stage Two—Moderate Communication Loss

At this stage, recall and word recognition decrease; attention span is shortened; digressions increase. (You may need to repeat the same question or sentence many times before it's understood.)

Closely related words are substituted for forgotten words—a new vocabulary to learn and respond to! When you can't make out what the patient needs, point while asking questions: "Do you want your sweater?" "Your necklace?"

The patient will have trouble understanding and following directions. Keep your sentences short and your directions clear. "Mother, fold the scarf." "Put the scarf in the drawer." "Close the drawer."

Delusions and Hallucinations

People with Alzheimer's sometimes have delusions and hallucinations.[19] Delusions are ideas that are not true. Hallucinations involve the senses—usually seeing or hearing things that are not there. For example, a mother at this stage may speak to her children—chatting with them or scolding them—even though the children are not in the room. Here are some ways to deal with patients who have hallucinations and delusions:

Make sure the patient can see and hear as well as possible. Check eyesight and hearing. Have the person wear glasses and/or a hearing aid. Have good lighting and try to eliminate any confusing noises.

If a delusion or hallucination isn't frightening or upsetting, ignoring it may be best for both of you.

Avoid contradicting or arguing with the person. Contradiction will only make the patient more upset, which will frustrate you.

Recognize the person's emotions and give comfort if you can. Say, "I can see that you're upset. Do you want a hug?"

Distraction sometimes helps. After a walk, the frightening hallucinations may be gone from your house.

False accusations—of unfaithfulness, for example—may result from a need for reassurance.

Find new ways to deal with these problems. For example, if the patient is anxiously awaiting the arrival of a long-dead mother, it may help to say that she called and she isn't coming today.

Remember that hallucinations and delusions may not be due to Alzheimer's. They might be a symptom of infection or other diseases. Call the patient's doctor. Even if they *are* due to dementia, the doctor may be able to control them with medication. Before prescribing medication, however, the doctor will determine whether the hallucinations or delusions are severe enough to call for drug therapy.

Stage Three—Severe Communication Loss

Toward the end, the patient with Alzheimer's loses almost all ability to communicate or understand. There are some things you can do to maintain lines of communication and connection with the patient.

Continue speaking warmly, quietly, and with eye-contact.

Pat or stroke the patient. Touch with love.

Smile. After all else is lost, a smile can calm and bring joy to the patient.

We become just
by performing just actions;
brave by performing brave actions.

Aristotle
(Greek philosopher)

Further Reading

Aronson MK, ed. *Understanding Alzheimer's Disease.* New York: Charles Scribner's Sons, 1988. A publication of the Alzheimer's Disease and Related Disorders Association.

Carroll DL. *When Your Loved One Has Alzheimer's: A Caregiver's Guide.* New York: Harper & Row/Perennial Library, 1990.

Chermak J. *Activities for Patients with Alzheimer's Disease and Related Disorders.* Available from the Hillhaven Corp, 1835 Union Avenue, Memphis, TN 38104.

Fish S. *Alzheimer's: Caring for Your Loved One, Caring for Yourself.* Chicago: Lion Publishing, 1990.

Jarvik L, Small G. *Parentcare: A Commonsense Guide for Adult Children.* New York: Crown Publishers, 1988.

Mace NL, Rabins PV. *The 36-Hour Day.* Baltimore: The Johns Hopkins University Press, 1991. Available from Warner Books, New York.

Support

CHAPTER 7

Support: Easing the Burden

*There is no hope of joy
except in human relations.*

Antoine de Saint-Exupery

(French novelist)

You don't have to do this alone. You'll need help caring for a family member or friend with Alzheimer's disease. Fortunately, you're not alone. There are many care organizations, support groups, and hotlines. There are people to help at home, centers outside home, and when the time comes, nursing homes away from home.

This section lists available help. For further information, talk to your physician, other healthcare professionals, your social worker, your next-door neighbor—the more people you talk to, the more help you'll hear about, and the more likely you'll be to find the help you need.

People and Places Who Can Help

Public agencies run by the state, city, or county can help—check your phone book or ask your physician.

Regional and local private organizations and charities have good sources also. So do support groups, senior citizen groups, religious groups, employers, friends, family, even neighbors. *Home healthcare agencies and visiting nurse associations* are excellent local starting points for health-related care.

Family and Friends

They are your first line of defense against loneliness, isolation, and too much caregiving. **Use them.** Ask for the help you need—accept whatever help is offered. Alzheimer's disease—any chronic illness—can bring families closer together or drive them apart. You could lose some old friends, but you will certainly add new and important friends as well.

Support Groups

Support groups range from a few people getting together to chat to large, formal organizations. They meet in living rooms, churches, hospitals, and nursing homes, to name a few.

What to expect from a support group. Many support groups provide a full range of help, from education to escorting patients on out-of-home appointments. Other groups are strictly discussion. There are groups for people with a patient at home, at a nursing or adult home, or in a hospital. There are caregiver groups, family groups, groups for teenagers, and even for toddlers. Choose the one that meets your needs. It will help you see you are not alone.

Locating a support group. The first place to go in finding a support group should be a local Alzheimer's disease association chapter, your doctor's office or clinic, or a local place of worship. Another organization that may help you is the National Self-Help Clearinghouse, Graduate School University Center, City University of New York, 33 West 42nd Street,

New York, NY 10036. The Clearinghouse keeps national listings of self-help groups and will provide referrals to meet your needs.

Remember, many people benefit from support groups, but you don't have to join a support group or even stay with one you've joined. Support groups are not for everyone, and the time is not always right for you to be a member.

Adult Day Care

Adult day-care programs provide a place where patients can be with other people in a supervised environment. These centers provide stimulating activities for patients while allowing caregivers to take a break. They are usually accredited or licensed by a government agency and may be affiliated with hospitals or nursing homes. Scheduling varies from "as needed" to regular, once-a-week, eight-hour days.

These programs can be found in more and more communities across the country. Not all of them, however, provide support for patients with serious cognitive and/or behavior problems. If you can't find

this kind of day-care setting, a regular senior citizens program may be helpful for the patient, but keep in mind that patients in the latter stage of Alzheimer's disease may have cognitive and behavior problems that may be very hard on other members who do not have these difficulties or who have different physical and emotional problems.

With the right adult day-care program, the caregiver can feel relieved, knowing the patient is receiving proper care and the opportunity to socialize and feel productive.

Support Professionals

There are many different types of professional services available to the caregiver in and out of the home. The list below describes some of these services. For some of them, it's possible to get financial assistance.

Registered nurses provide nursing care. They are trained, accredited, and licensed by the state—and available on an as-needed basis. One source for finding a qualified registered nurse is the local Visiting Nurse Association (see page 100).

Social workers evaluate the caregiver's and the patient's needs, then make referrals and provide counseling. Most have graduate degrees and are accredited by the state.

Home health aides provide personal care for patients, helping with medication, exercises, and the monitoring of vital signs. Some help with household tasks such as shopping and cooking. They are usually trained in programs given by their agency and are available either on a daily basis or for agreed-upon hours.

Homemakers perform household duties—general cleaning, laundry services, and a few extras like taking out garbage and unpacking groceries. They are trained through their agency and are available once or twice a week.

Live-in aides provide general care like light housekeeping, with little or no nursing care. They are trained by their agency and available for agreed-upon hours.

Drivers will accompany you and your patient in the car, carrying packages and bags, helping with walkers or wheelchairs, and often pushing shopping carts and opening doors. A special motor vehicle license may be necessary for this job—be sure to ask.

Adult homes provide short-term care—overnight or for several weeks or a month—to give caregivers a much needed break. They're often small, family owned homes accredited or licensed by a government agency. Available "as needed."

Hospitals may also provide short-term or daytime care.

What if something happens to you? You'll need help immediately if something happens to you or another member of your care "team." So plan ahead. Carry identification. Include the name and number of the other caregiver who's agreed to pinch-hit for you if, for some reason, you're unable to care for your loved one.

Make plans—before help is needed—for someone to take over your responsibilities.

Take care of yourself. Your physical and emotional health are really important.

Nursing Homes

A special note: The nursing home decision should not be a decision of "last" resort but of "best" resort. Placement in a home may very well improve the patient's care and safety.

The right time to consider a nursing home depends on the health and needs of the patient, on *your* health and *your* needs, and on the needs of the family.

Talk to people—especially to your support group—and then consult family members. Share the decision.

Most people decide on a nursing home when incontinence, unsafe acts, and wandering become insurmountable problems.

It's a painful decision—but the pain can be lessened by knowing you've made the right decision. The information below may help clear the way.

Three Types of Nursing Homes

Nursing homes can be operated as a business, as a nonprofit religious or community facility, or as a nonprofit government agency. And it's important to keep in mind that the terminology for many long-term care facilities differs from state to state. For example, some states use the terms "assisted living," "community based residential," and "sheltered care." But no matter what they are called or how they are run, there are three general types of nursing homes.

A skilled nursing facility provides 24-hour care by registered nurses and other staff members. The term "skilled nursing care" is **important.** It refers to both the facility and the amount of financial aid available through government and private insurers. There are **specific** medical indications for **skilled** nursing care including medical necessities such as wound dress-

ings, incontinence, and degree of dependence and incapacity. Patients who do not fit those specific indications will not, in some states, be permitted a "bed" at a skilled nursing facility.

A health-related facility provides care for a patient not in need of skilled nursing care but needing some personal nursing attention, medical aid, and a protected environment. "Health-related" is also a semi-legal term defining the degree of care necessary and the amount of aid possible. The term "intermediate-care facility" is used in some places.

A combined facility provides both types of care with step-ups possible as necessary.

All Nursing Homes Provide Three Types of Service

Personal health care: all medicines, therapies, and general medical care.

Personal nursing care: help with daily routine, including bathing, dressing, toileting, moving around, and eating.

Domestic care: provision of room, food, care of clothing, beauty shop (in most states), recreation, and general environment.

The Right Home

Finding another home for a person you love is a difficult, often painful, process.

The topic can and does fill books; a good one to start with is *Choosing a Nursing Home for the Person with Intellectual Loss,* edited by E. Lincoln, published in 1980 by the Burke Rehabilitation Center. You can get it through the Alzheimer's Disease and Related Disorders Association.

The American Health Care Association provides a checklist for evaluating nursing homes that can be invaluable. You can contact the AHCA at 1201 L Street, NW, Washington, DC, 20005; 202-842-4444.

Choosing a Nursing Home

Do your investigation long before you think you may need a home. Advance planning will help you provide for the necessary decisions without pressure.

Get recommendations and help in filling out the mountains of forms—from hospital, agency, or private-practice social workers.

Visit the homes with a relative or friend. Don't go alone. It's too hard. Visit any home you are considering more than once; see everything.

Accept the fact that no nursing home is perfect and that other people provide care differently from the way you do. If you have a negative experience on your first few visits to nursing homes, wait a few days and try again. Revisit homes you have rejected for nonessential reasons.

Check the facts, but trust your intuition, too.
After care and safety, the deciding factor will probably be the way you respond to a home and the people in it.

Deciding Where to Visit

These factors can help you decide which nursing homes to visit:

Convenient location. You'll be able to visit more easily and so will other relatives and friends.

Size. How many beds is the right size? A smaller home may seem more "homey." Bigger homes may have more activities and more specialized staff.

Medical services. Are the costs included? What about visits from personal physicians?

Residents. Is there a special unit for patients with Alzheimer's? Would the person you are caring for be more comfortable with other similar patients, or would a variety provide more stimulation? Fellow residents from similar ethnic and religious backgrounds may also help a patient with Alzheimer's feel at home.

Policies and Personnel

Questions to ask the nursing home representative:

Admission. Is there a waiting list? Can you fill out forms in advance? Will the patient need a physical exam before admission? Who should do it?

Finances. Is the nursing home eligible for Medicare and Medicaid? What services are included and what costs are extra?

Medical. Is a registered nurse on the premises at all times? Is a doctor in-house or on call? What is the backup hospital? Does the facility have any discharge criteria?

Taking the Tour

Things to notice as you walk around the nursing home include:

The building. Is it clean, reasonably odor free, well lit, attractive?

Safety. The safety features described earlier apply to nursing homes as well. In addition, they should have clearly marked exits, fire extinguishers, a sprinkler system, nonskid floor surfaces, and recent records of state and local inspections you can review.

Does the home seem like a busy place? Residents should be occupied; staff should be active and involved—and pleasant to each other and the residents.

Cleanliness counts. Is the home clean? Are the staff members clean and neat? (Look in stairways as well as major living areas.)

Residents. Are most of them up and dressed in clean clothes each day? Are they occupied? If residents are in bed or restrained, is it for their benefit or for staff convenience?

Food. Is there a dietitian on staff? Are the portions big enough? Is the food good—and good for you? Is there help for people who have trouble eating? Is there a dining room (good for social life), or do residents eat in their rooms (good for the patient who is easily distracted from eating)?

Activities. Are they frequent and interesting? Is there an activity room? Is it well equipped? Are there outings?

Rooms of residents. No more than four residents to a room? Can your person bring furniture, pictures, plants, or other things? Is there a closet and chest of drawers? Is there privacy for dressing, phone calls, visits?

NOTE: **The checklist below refers to the previous discussion about choosing a nursing home. Use this checklist to ensure that you address all the major issues related to selecting a nursing home.**

Choosing a Nursing Home

❏ If you feel you need it, ask for help in filling out forms—from hospital, agency, or private-practice social workers.

❏ Visited the nursing homes with a relative or friend.

❏ Checked all the facts and available information about the homes.

❏ Convenient location—it will be easy for you and other family members and friends to visit.

❏ Size—it meets your concerns and the patient's needs.

❏ Medical services—you've checked to see how the costs are structured; for example, is there an extra charge for visits from personal physicians?

❏ Residents—does the medical, ethnic, religious makeup of residents meet your concerns and the patient's needs? Is there a special unit for patients with Alzheimer's?

Policies and Personnel

- [ ] Admission—you've learned everything about the admission policy and procedure.
- [ ] Finances—you have reviewed the payment policy and learned whether the home is eligible for Medicare and Medicaid.
- [ ] Medical—you are aware of all physician/nurse help available and how often it is available; and you are aware of all the equipment, special help, and procedures involved in patient care.

Taking the Tour

- [ ] The building is clean, reasonably odor free, well-lit, attractive.
- [ ] Safety—you've checked that the staff cares about its patients' safety; for example, there are clearly marked exits, fire extinguishers, a sprinkler system, nonskid floor surfaces, and frequent state and local inspections.
- [ ] There are plenty of activities for patients, and the staff and residents are pleasant to each other
- [ ] The facilities and staff members are clean and neat.
- [ ] Food—there is a dietitian on staff, the portions are big enough, the dining room is pleasant, and there is proper support for people who have trouble eating.
- [ ] Rooms—there are no more than four residents to a room, and you have learned what the patient can keep in the room, such as furniture, pictures, plants, or other things.

Alternative Institutions

Mental hospitals, private and public, have beds that can be used for patients with Alzheimer's. Although the thought of a mental hospital may be disturbing, the care is often very fine with a skilled, caring staff.

Foster care. There are some state and private foster home plans that place patients with families when the patient is not in need of skilled nursing care, not incontinent, and is ambulatory.

Hospices. Hospice care is available through government and private agencies for Alzheimer's patients in the terminal stage of the illness. Hospice care can either be at a separate facility or can be provided within the home by an agency such as the Visiting Nurses Association.

Organizations That Can Help

The Center for Medical Consumers & Health Care Information
237 Thompson Street
New York, NY 10012
212-674-7105

The center has a newsletter, *Health Facts,* and provides up-to-date information for individual home-care needs. In addition, the center has a topical lending library and a counseling service.

Two of the most important organizations you may need are:

Alzheimer's Disease Education and Referral Center
(ADEAR)
PO Box 8250
Silver Spring, MD 20907
800-438-4380

Provides information about Alzheimer's disease diagnosis, treatment, and research to health professionals and the public.

Alzheimer's Disease and Related Disorders Association
(The Alzheimer's Association or ADRDA)
919 North Michigan
Chicago, IL 60601
312-335-8700

Promotes research for Alzheimer's disease and provides educational programs for the public; works to develop family support systems for relatives of victims of the disease. There are also many local chapters that can provide help with state laws, etc. Look in your phone book.

Organized Help

Accent on Information
PO Box 700
Bloomington, IL 61702
309-378-2961

A computerized retrieval system designed to help disabled persons live more effective lives by offering access to information on problems, issues of concern, and products and services available to the handicapped.

Administration on Aging
330 Independence Avenue, SW, Room 4760
Washington, DC 20201
202-619-0724

Information and referral service that provides assess-
ment of home-care needs. Provides support for elderly people in whatever area of assistance is needed.

American Association of Homes for the Aging
901 E Street, NW
Washington, DC 20049
202-783-2242

Provides services—including group discount and
insurance plans and educational and informational
programs—to persons 55 and older.

American Federation of Home Health Agencies
1320 Fenwick Lane, Suite 100
Silver Spring, MD 20910
301-588-1454

Agencies providing services such as nursing, speech
therapy, and physical therapy in the home. Presents
the concerns of home health agencies to Congress
and to the Health Care Financing Administration.
Conducts 15 to 20 seminars per year on home health
issues and laws.

The National Council on the Aging
409 Third Street, SW, Suite 400
Washington, DC 20024
202-479-1200

Cooperates with other organizations to promote concern for older people and develop methods and
resources for meeting their needs.

Provides a national information and consultation center; holds conferences and workshops. Maintains a
library of 14,000 volumes on aging, with emphasis on
the psychological, economic, and social aspects of
the subject.

National Council of Senior Citizens
1331 F Street, NW
Washington, DC 20004
202-347-8800

Publishes monthly newsletter covering legislation pertaining to senior citizens; gold-card members are offered an in-house hospitalization plan, Medicare supplement insurance, and pharmacy prescription discounts.

National Institute on Aging
US Department of Health and Human Services
9000 Rockville Pike
Building 31, Room 5C35
Bethesda, MD 20892-3100
301-496-9265

The institute conducts and supports research to increase the knowledge of the aging process.

National Rehabilitation Information Center
8455 Colesville Road, Suite 935
Silver Spring, MD 20910-3319
301-588-9284
1-800-346-2742

Referral center for independent living as a disabled person; has database of articles and books and can perform literature searches for a fee.

Visiting Nurse Associations of America
3801 E Florida Avenue, Suite 900
Denver, CO 80210
303-753-0218

Association of voluntary, nonprofit home healthcare agencies that work to strengthen business resources and economic programs through marketing and contracting. Offers workshops and training programs.

Hotlines

The hot lines listed here are for national services. For local hot line information, check your phone book.

Alcohol Abuse Hot Line: 1-800-ALCOHOL (252-6465)

CONTACT Teleministries USA: 717-652-4400
(Free telephone counseling and crisis intervention)

Health Care Financing: 1-800-638-6833
(U.S. Dept. of Health and Human Services)

Home Care Hot Line: 202-547-7424
(Provided by the National Association for Home Care)

Pain Control Hot Line: 703-368-7357

Suicide Hot Line: 213-381-5111
(Immediate counseling and referral)

Surgical Second Opinion Hot Line: 1-800-638-6833
(Information and referral service sponsored by U.S. government)

Products That Can Help

There are a great number of products, devices, and services that can make your life at home with your patient easier and safer. The sources below have cat-alogues you can send for. (Inclusion on this list does not necessarily imply approval or recommendation by the publisher or distributor of this guide.)

Safety Aids

Medic-Alert is a bracelet identification system, linked to a 24-hour office, that provides full information about the wearer in case of emergency. The Medic-Alert Foundation International is in Turlock, California.

Round-the-Clock Multiple Time Switch can be programmed to stop or start household appliances. Available from American Foundation for the Blind.

A one-way intercom, or a baby intercom, will let you listen to the activities of the patient with Alzheimer's without being heard yourself. They are available in most electronics stores.

Personal Care Aids

Easy eating utensils, including plates with suction cups, no-tip glasses and cups, high-sided dishes, and separate suction cups, are available from Fred Sammons. Call 1-800-323-5547.

Incontinence pants and underpads are available at many pharmacies and supermarkets. If you have a prescription for them, they may be reimbursable.

A pill organizer will help the correct dispensing of pills each week. Pill organizers are available from medical supply firms or pharmacies.

A bedside chair with a concealed toilet should be available through local pharmacy supply stores in your area.

Aids from Medical Supply Houses

Home blood-pressure monitors are provided if your physician advises one.

Dental emergency kits provide short-term relief from simple dental problems.

Bed clothes, pillows, and torso supports improve sleep and prevent bed sores.

Wheelchairs and walkers facilitate mobility.

Source for Healthcare Equipment

Fred Sammons, Inc. 1-800-323-5547. Will send catalogue upon request.

Direct Purchase Sources

American Foundation for the Blind; 212-620-2000. Ask for Consumer Products Catalogue.

Sears Home Health Care; 800-326-1750 or see local Sears branch.

*Make yourself
necessary
to someone.*

Ralph Waldo Emerson
(American philosopher)

Further Reading

Alzheimer's Disease, Especially for Teenagers. Alzheimer's Association (ADRDA).

American National Red Cross Home Nursing Textbook. New York: Doubleday, 1979.

Bruer J. *Handbook of Assistive Devices for the Handicapped Aged.* New York: Haworth Press, 1982.

Calder A, Watt A. *I Love You but You Drive Me Crazy: A Guide for Caring Relatives.* Vancouver, Canada: Forbez, 1981.

Cohen D, Eisdorfer C. *The Loss of Self: A Family Resource for the Care of Alzheimer's Disease and Related Disorders.* New York: W. W. Norton, 1986.

Guthrie D. *Grandpa Doesn't Know It's Me.* New York: Human Science Press, 1986.

Hooker S. *Caring for Elderly People.* London: Routledge & Kegan Paul, 1981.

Karr K. *What Do I Do: How to Care for, Comfort, and Commune With Your Nursing Home Elder.* New York: Haworth Press, 1985.

Safford F. *Caring for the Mentally Impaired Elderly.* New York: Holt, Rinehart and Winston, 1986.

Profile

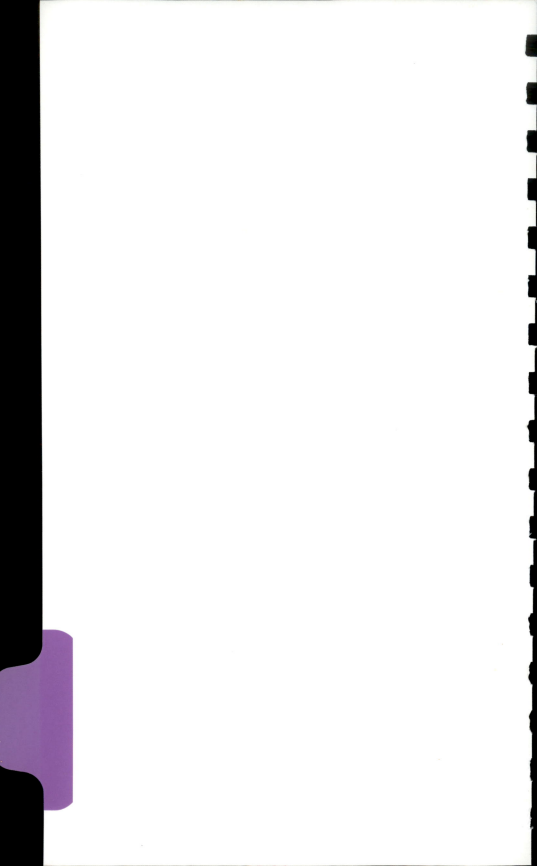

CHAPTER 8

The Patient Profile

*All the beautiful sentiments
in the world weigh less than
a single lovely action.*
James Russell Lowell
(American poet)

This chapter is designed for you to use to pass vital information on to a caregiver who may substitute for you or take your place entirely someday. Fill out the spaces indicated with everything someone has to know to take your place as caregiver. Then, whether you're taking a break or finished caregiving completely, you can relax, recharge, renew.

Suggestions

- Go through each section. Take your time. Think carefully about a typical day and your loved one's special needs.

- Once you've filled everything out, check again in a few days to see if you remember something you left out the first time.

- Use *pencil.* Things change; schedules, medicines, physical abilities, etc. You may even need to change things more than once.

- You may not need all the spaces provided. You may need more. Do what works for you and your patient—make notes, draw pictures, whatever it takes to share your caregiver responsibilities.

The Patient Profile

General Information

Patient Name_____

Address_____

Home Tele. # _____

Caregiver _____

Address_____

Home Tele. # _____

Emergency Tele. #s

1._____

2._____

3._____

4._____

5._____

6._____

Medication Schedule

1. **Medication**_____

    _____   _____   ☐   ☐
    TImes per Day   **Time of Day Taken**   **With   Without**
                                                    Food   Food

2. **Medication**_____

    _____   _____   ☐   ☐
    TImes per Day   **Time of Day Taken**   **With   Without**
                                                    Food   Food

3. **Medication**_____

    _____   _____   ☐   ☐
    TImes per Day   **Time of Day Taken**   **With   Without**
                                                    Food   Food

4. **Medication**_____

    _____   _____   ☐   ☐
    TImes per Day   **Time of Day Taken**   **With   Without**
                                                    Food   Food

5. **Medication**_____

    _____   _____   ☐   ☐
    TImes per Day   **Time of Day Taken**   **With   Without**
                                                    Food   Food

6. **Medication**_____

    _____   _____   ☐   ☐
    TImes per Day   **Time of Day Taken**   **With   Without**
                                                    Food   Food

Activities Schedule

MONDAY

Morning _____

Afternoon _____

Evening _____

TUESDAY

Morning _____

Afternoon _____

Evening _____

WEDNESDAY

Morning _____

Afternoon _____

Evening _____

THURSDAY

Morning _____

Afternoon _____

Evening _____

FRIDAY

Morning _____

Afternoon _____

Evening _____

SATURDAY

Morning _____

Afternoon _____

Evening _____

SUNDAY

Morning _____

Afternoon _____

Evening _____

(Don't forget other activities like day-care nurse and social worker visits, deliveries, etc.)

Visitors Who May Drop By

1._____

2._____

3._____

4._____

5._____

6._____

Don't Be Surprised If...

(Describe any strange or odd behavior patterns.)

1._____

_____

_____

2._____

_____

_____

3._____

_____

_____

4._____

_____

_____

5._____

_____

_____

6._____

_____

Patient May Need...

	Yes	No	Where to Find
Glasses	❑	❑	_____
Hearing Aid	❑	❑	_____
Special Shoes/Socks	❑	❑	_____
Dentures	❑	❑	_____
Walker	❑	❑	_____

Other _____

_____

_____

_____

_____

_____

_____

These Things May Agitate the Patient

1._____

_____

2._____

_____

3._____

_____

4._____

_____

5._____

_____

6._____

_____

If The Patient Becomes Distressed or Agitated...

The following may help calm the patient down:

❏ **Special Reassuring Phrases** _____

_____

_____

❏ **Cup of Tea (flavor)**_____

❏ **Television (program)**_____

❏ **Radio (program)**_____

❏ **Special Medication**
(List name, dosage, and where stored.)

_____

_____

_____

_____

❏ **Other**_____

_____

_____

_____

_____

_____

Wake-up Routine

_____
(Patient name)

usually wakes up at:_____

First activity on a typical morning:

❏ Bath

❏ Shower

❏ Sponge bath

❏ Toilet

❏ Dress

❏ Other _____

Where this activity happens:

❏ Bathroom

❏ Bedside

❏ Other_____

Special items needed at this time:

- ☐ Cane
- ☐ Walker
- ☐ Bedpan
- ☐ Hearing aid
- ☐ Dentures
- ☐ Other_____

Where these items are usually kept:

- ☐ Bathroom cabinet
- ☐ Closet
- ☐ Other_____

_____

_____

The patient wears:

- ☐ Medication tags
- ☐ Medic-Alert device
- ☐ Other_____

_____

_____

Medications to be taken before breakfast (Note difficulties in swallowing the medication—or special items needed):

1._____

_____

2._____

_____

3._____

_____

4._____

_____

5._____

_____

6._____

_____

Patient is able to dress him/herself:

❑ Yes

❑ No - Needs Help (Describe necessary help.)

_____

_____

_____

_____

_____

_____

Where necessary clothing items are stored:

❑ Closet (location)_____

❑ Chest of drawers (location)_____

❑ Other_____

_____

_____

_____

At Breakfast...

Does patient have breakfast before or
after he/she is dressed?

❏ Before

❏ After

❏ Other_____

_____

_____

_____

Breakfast time: _____

Patient usually eats breakfast in the:

❏ Kitchen

❏ Dining room

❏ Bedroom

❏ Other_____

Favorite breakfast items:

❏ Cereal (type or brand name)_____

_____

_____

❏ Toast (type or brand name)_____

❑ Other _____

_____

_____

_____

Does patient participate in breakfast preparation?

❑ Yes

❑ No

If yes, list what they do: _____

_____

_____

_____

Medications to be taken during or after breakfast

1. _____

_____

2. _____

_____

3. _____

_____

4. _____

5._____

_____

6._____

_____

Special utensils needed

☐ Yes

☐ No

If yes, list what they are:_____

_____

_____

_____

Other important information:

_____

_____

_____

_____

Morning Activities

After breakfast:

❏ **Television (list programs)** _____

_____

_____

❏ **A walk (list places)** _____

_____

_____

❏ **Reading**

❏ **Being read to**

❏ **Other** _____

_____

_____

_____

Favorite spot to sit:

❏ **Chair (location)** _____

❏ **Couch (location)** _____

❏ **Other** _____

_____

_____

Favorite hobbies or entertainment:

❏ Read

❏ Talk on phone

❏ Watch TV (list programs) _____

_____

_____

❏ Other _____

_____

_____

A morning nap?

❏ Yes

❏ No

If yes, list time and where patient likes to nap: ___

_____

_____

_____

A midmorning snack?

❑ Yes

❑ No

If yes, list time: _____

Favorite snacks: _____

_____

_____

Other important information: _____

_____

_____

_____

_____

_____

_____

_____

_____

Lunch

What time? _____

Where?

    ❑ **Kitchen**

    ❑ **Dining room**

    ❑ **Bedroom**

    ❑ **Other room**_____

Favorite or typical lunch foods:

    ❑ **Sandwich (list favorites)** _____

    _____

    _____

    _____

    ❑ **Soup (list favorites)**_____

_____

_____

_____

    ❑ **Other**_____

    _____

    _____

Is patient used to a diversion?

❏ **Television (list program)**_____

_____

❏ **Radio (list program)**_____

_____

❏ **Other**_____

_____

_____

Medications to be taken during or after lunch:

1._____

_____

2._____

_____

3._____

_____

4._____

_____

5._____

_____

6._____

_____

Special utensils needed

    ❏ Yes

    ❏ No

        If yes, list what they are:_____

        _____

        _____

        _____

Other important information:

_____

_____

_____

_____

_____

Afternoon Activities

Special activities after lunch:

❑ **Television (list programs)** _____

_____

_____

❑ **A walk (list places)** _____

_____

_____

❑ **Reading**

❑ **Being read to**

❑ **Other** _____

_____

_____

_____

Favorite spot to sit:

❑ **Chair (location)** _____

❑ **Couch (location)** _____

❑ **Other** _____

_____

_____

An afternoon nap?

❏ Yes

❏ No

If yes, list time and where patient likes to nap: ___

_____

_____

_____

An afternoon snack?

❏ Yes

❏ No

If yes, list time: _____

Favorite snacks: _____

_____

_____

Other important information: _____

_____

_____

_____

At Dinner

What time? _____

Where?

❏ Kitchen

❏ Dining room

❏ In front of TV

❏ Other room_____

Favorite dinner foods:

1._____

_____

2._____

_____

3._____

4._____

_____

5._____

_____

Does patient need help with dinner?

❏ Yes

❏ No

If yes, describe:_____

_____

_____

_____

Medications to be taken during or after dinner:

1._____

_____

2._____

_____

3._____

_____

4._____

_____

5._____

_____

6._____

_____

Special utensils needed:

❑ Yes

❑ No

If yes, list what they are:_____

_____

_____

_____

Other important information:

_____

_____

_____

_____

_____

Evening Activities

Special after-dinner activities:

❏ Walk (where) _____

❏ TV (what programs)_____

_____

_____

❏ Regular visitors _____

_____

_____

_____

❏ Call friend/relative _____

_____

_____

❏ Other _____

_____

_____

An evening snack?

❑ Yes

❑ No

    If yes, list time: _____

    Favorite snacks: _____

    _____

    _____

Evening medications:

1._____

_____

2._____

_____

3._____

_____

4._____

_____

5._____

_____

6._____

Other important information: _____

_____

_____

_____

_____

_____

_____

_____

Bedtime Routine

Usual bedtime is: _____

Patient is able to undress

    ❏ Yes

    ❏ No

        If no, describe help needed: _____

        _____

        _____

        _____

Where night clothes are stored:_____

_____

_____

_____

_____

_____

_____

Nightly Dental Routine

Dentures

❏ Yes

❏ No

If yes, is cleaning necessary? _____

Nightly shower/bath needed?

❏ Yes

❏ No

If yes, describe:_____

_____

_____

Medication taken at bedtime:

1._____

_____

2._____

_____

3._____

_____

4._____

5._____

_____

6._____

_____

Other important information: _____

_____

_____

Special items needed:

❏ Adult diaper/incontinence pad

❏ Urinal/bedpan

❏ Special pillows/blankets

❏ Night-light

❏ Music/radio/TV

❏ Other_____

_____

_____

_____

Be on the Alert for...

❑ Patient may wake up and "wander"

Note any of the following:

❑ Special gates at door/on stairs

❑ Special locks/keys/alarms

❑ Other _____

_____

_____

_____

_____

_____

_____

Note any of the following:

❑ Special medications _____

_____

_____

_____

❑ Special restraints if necessary _____

_____

_____

❏ **Other calming techniques** _____

_____

_____

_____

_____

_____

_____

If Anything Happens, You Can Call...

I can be reached at the following telephone numbers:

1._____

2._____

3._____

Nurses' or social workers' numbers:

1._____

2._____

Hospital numbers:

1._____

2._____

Physicians:

1._____

2._____

3._____

Pharmacy numbers:

1._____

2._____

Police:_____

Fire Department: _____

Other important numbers:

_____

_____

_____

_____

_____

_____

Favorite Activities

- ❏ Walk

- ❏ Read (or be read to)

- ❏ Watch TV

- ❏ Hobbies

- ❏ Talk/tell stories

- ❏ Other _____

_____

_____

_____

_____

_____

_____

Special Skills

❏ **Plays instrument**

    If yes, please list: _____

    _____

❏ **Gardening**

❏ **Other** _____

    _____

    _____

    _____

    _____

    _____

    _____

    _____

    _____

Strange Words or Expressions and What They Mean

1._____

_____

_____

2._____

_____

_____

3._____

_____

_____

4._____

_____

_____

5._____

_____

_____

6._____

_____

Notes

Glossary

Use these pages as a review of some of the terms mentioned in this book.

ACh — acetylcholine is one of a group of important chemicals in brain cells; responsible for the ability to remember because it helps transmit messages from one brain cell to another

Adult day-care — centers that have a supervised environment where patients can be with others in a social situation

Adult homes — small centers for short-term care (overnight up to several weeks); usually licensed by the government or the state, and may offer different services depending on the state or region

Alzheimer, Dr. Alois — physician who first described the kind of dementia now known as Alzheimer's disease

Alzheimer's disease — dementia that causes a serious decline of intellectual functions, including memory, the ability to think, and motor skills

The Alzheimer's Association — organization based in Chicago that promotes research of Alzheimer's disease and educational programs for families of victims

Barbiturates — drugs used for their sedative or anti-spasmodic effects

Brain autopsy — examination performed by a physician on a deceased person; the only definitive way to diagnose Alzheimer's disease

Brain deterioration — condition of a brain that no longer has its normal abilities; the inability to function mentally as well as one did in the past

Cognex® (tacrine hydrochloride capsules) — a drug for the treatment of probable mild-to-moderate Alzheimer's disease

Combined facility — building with healthcare professionals who provide both personal care and skilled nursing care

Conservator — person designated with the power to take over and protect the interests of one who is incompetent

CPA — certified public accountant; one who helps people manage money or prepare tax forms

Dementia — condition in a person that is marked by an incapacitating decline of intellectual abilities, including memory and the ability to think

Disorientation — condition in a person that is marked by mental confusion, especially as to time, place, or identity

Domestic care — service offered by people who are trained; services include being provided a room, food, care of clothing, recreation, and a generally healthy environment

Drivers — people who provide transportation, carry packages, help with wheelchairs

Durable power of attorney — a legal document giving another person authority to make financial and legal decisions even if the principal becomes physically or mentally incompetent

Elder care lawyers — attorneys trained to provide the information and aid most necessary to elderly people

Elder law — field of law that deals with the complexities and issues of the elderly

Estate planning — process that includes planning for the present and future use of assets

Fair value — items or services that qualify as valuable and "allowable" ways of using up assets to qualify for Medicaid; as long as "fair value" is received, assets can be "spent down" to meet eligibility requirement (Large gifts cannot be given to become instantly eligible.)

Foster care — care in which patients are placed with a family if no skilled nursing care is needed

Guardian — person who is designated as having the protective care of another person or that person's property

Hallucinations — condition that includes "seeing" or "hearing" something that is not there

Hardening of the arteries — arteriosclerosis, or an abnormal thickening of the artery walls, causing a loss of elasticity and problems with blood flow

Healthcare agent — a person who accepts the power to make healthcare decisions for someone else

Healthcare proxy — a delegation of authority to a healthcare agent

Health-related facility — building with professionals who provide personal nursing care for patients not in need of skilled nursing care, but services may vary from state to state

Heimlich maneuver — method of clearing the airway of a choking person

Home health aides — people who provide personal care and help with medications, exercises, and monitoring of vital signs

Homemakers — people who provide household help—cleaning, laundry; trained and supplied through an agency

Hospice — facility or program designed to provide a positive environment for the terminally ill

Incurable disease — illness that cannot be reversed by medication or other treatment

Joint bank account — bank account that has two owners who have full access to the funds

Live-in aides — people who provide general care and light housekeeping, with little or no nursing care

Living trust — a contract between a person who owns property and a person selected to manage that property

Living will — document that describes preferences for medical steps to be taken if the person becomes unable to make decisions

Martyr — person who gives up one's life for another

Medic-Alert — bracelet identification system, linked to a 24-hour service, that provides full information in case of emergency

Medicaid — program insured by the US government and run by each state; assistance in covering medical expenses is furnished on the basis of financial need

Medicare — program insured by the US government and designed to cover medical costs for people who are over 65 or disabled

Mental hospitals — institutions designed to meet the needs of mentally unstable or incapacitated individuals through a specially trained staff

Paranoia — term used to describe a person who falsely believes that he is being persecuted; one of the most common symptoms of Alzheimer's disease

Parke-Davis — company that makes pharmaceuticals; the manufacturer of Cognex® (tacrine hydrochloride capsules)

Personal nursing care — helping people with bathing, dressing, toileting, and eating

Power of attorney (also "durable power of attorney") — power a person has to authorize and manage the legal and/or financial affairs of another in the event of that person's incapacitation or unavailability

Registered nurse — nurse with a graduate degree who has been licensed by the state after passing a state exam—also called an RN

Skilled nursing facility — institution with people who provide 24-hour nursing care by registered nurses

Social inhibition — term used to describe self-control; appropriate behavior in social situations

Social workers — people who evaluate needs for referrals and counseling; help locate paid or unpaid services as needed

Spending down — term that means spending or disposing of assets so that they are reduced to a level that qualifies one for Medicaid

Sundowning — behavior marked by late afternoon wandering or pacing; typical of Alzheimer's patients

Support groups — groups of people who get together to share common experiences

Tacrine hydrochloride — (drug; see Cognex®)

Testamentary capacity — term that means the legal competence to know one is making a will, including what property there is to distribute and the names and relationships of the people getting the property

Thyroid — gland at the base of the throat that produces a hormone which influences growth, development, and metabolic rate

Will — document drawn up by a person that legally declares how to dispose of the person's property after death

References

1. Wells CE. Organic syndromes: dementia. In: Kaplan HI, Sadock BJ, eds. *Comprehensive Textbook of Psychiatry.* 4th ed. Baltimore, MD: Williams & Wilkins; 1985:851.

2. Drachman DA, Friedland RP, Larson EB, et al. Making sure it's really Alzheimer's. *Patient Care.* 1991;25(18):13-40.

3. Gilley DW, Wilson RS, Bennett DA, et al. Cessation of driving and unsafe motor vehicle operation by dementia patients. *Arch Intern Med.* 1991;151:941-946.

4. Friedland RP, Koss E, Kuman A, et al. Motor vehicle crashes in dementia of the Alzheimer's type. *Ann Neurol.* 1988;24:782-786.

5. Deutsch LH, Rovner BW. Agitation and other noncognitive abnormalities in Alzheimer's disease. *Psychiatr Clin North Am.* 1991;14:341-351.

6. Masters WH, Johnson VE, Kolodny RC. *Human Sexuality.* 4th ed. New York, NY: Harper Collins Publishers; 1992:576.

7. Brown MM, Hachinski VC. Acute confusional states, amnesia, and dementia. In: Wilson JD, ed. *Harrison's Principles of Internal Medicine.* 12th ed. New York, NY: McGraw-Hill; 1991:190.

8. *The 1992 Information Please Almanac.* New York, NY: Houghton Mifflin Company; 1992:85-87.

9. Bartus RT, Dean RL, Flicker C. Cholinergic psychopharmacology: an integration of human and animal research on memory. In: Meltzer HY, ed. *Psychopharmacology: The Third Generation of Progress.* New York, NY: The Raven Press; 1987:219-220.

10. Selkoe DJ. Molecular pathology of amyloidogenic proteins and the role of amyloids in Alzheimer's disease. *Neurobiol Aging.* 1989;10:387-395.

11. Breitner JCS. Clinical genetics and genetic counseling in Alzheimer's disease. *Ann Intern Med.* 1991;115:601-606.

12. Perl DP, Good PF. Uptake of aluminum into central nervous system along nasal-olfactory pathways. *Lancet.* 1987;1:1028.

13. Prusiner SB. Molecular biology of prion diseases. *Science.* 1991;252:1515-1522.

14. Joachim CL, Morris JH, Selkoe DJ. Clinically diagnosed Alzheimer's disease: autopsy results in 150 cases. *Ann Neurol.* 1988;24:50-56.

15. Vestal RE. General principles of geriatric medical practice: Clinical pharmacology. In: Kelly WN, eds. *Textbook of Internal Medicine.* Philadelphia, PA: JB Lippincott Co; 1987:2622-2623.

16. Mozar HN, Bal DG, Howard JT. Perspectives on the etiology of Alzheimer's disease. *JAMA.* 1987;257:1503-1507.

17. Davies P, Katzman R, Price D, et al. AD research: what's new and important. *Patient Care.* 1991;25(8):139-169.

18. Strauss PJ, ESQ. Reconciliation Act (1993), Section 13611 and 13612 (Written communication).

19. Wragg RE, Jeste DV. Neuroleptics and alternative treatments: management of behavioral symptoms and psychosis in Alzheimer's disease and related conditions. *Psychiatr Clin North Am*. 1988; 11:195-213.